CW00823214

This enriching book opens with a helpful overview ⟨...⟩ therapy theory and practice with people with learn⟨...⟩ amples from a wide range of contexts and from in⟨...⟩ engaging descriptions of dramatherapy sessions whi⟨...⟩ the clients themselves. It is packed with significant discussions and vivid examples for practitioners such as supporting a child with the birth of a new sibling, working systemically, addressing mental ill-health and bereavement needs. It is infused with a passion for equality of access, giving rise to genuine inclusivity for people with learning disabilities.

Mandy Carr, former senior lecturer in dramatherapy, dramatherapist and
clinical supervisor

The many voices in this book shed light on the depth and attention that drama-therapists afford their clients of diverse abilities and how, in return our clients offer riches back to the profession itself. It's an effective snapshot of the life of drama-therapy with people with learning disabilities. The reader will enter the unknown, and experience the carving of an empowering story of how the exploration of the imagination and its healing powers is open and accessible to all humans. The thera-peutic practices outlined here are as kaleidoscopic as our client group.

Dimpi Hirani MA, MSc., dramatherapist and clinical supervisor. Founder
of a special needs school service and former convenor of the
BADth Education Sub-Committee.

This timely publication is a valuable resource for a wide range of professionals, trainers and trainees working in the field of learning disabilities across the life cycle in education, health and Third Sector settings. Accounts of dramatherapy practice include advocacy interventions with non-verbal clients and together the contribu-tions show that the presence of client voice and agency is strong in this publication which promotes a good number of first time authors. Evaluating outcomes and the impact of dramatherapy in a specialist child service and the range of multi-disci-plinary collaborations across specialist settings are strengths of this publication. A valuable contribution to the field of dramatherapy research, practice and theory.

Emma Ramsden is a Practitioner-researcher (dramatherapy)

This is a magnificent book! A welcome addition to the series, of value to practition-ers, service users, carers and colleagues and a book that will become a key text for this important area of practice. We venture with the authors into the therapeutic space, reading compelling examples of Dramatherapists' work to construct crea-tive, safe spaces for deep therapeutic work. We share the joy and the challenges of their work and – importantly – hear service users' voices speak powerfully. This book shows commitment to valuing and learning from difference, to empowerment and activism; it encourages reflective, creative, authentic dramatherapy and inter-professional practice. An invaluable addition to the literature that comprehensively fills the gap on our bookshelves, and that I highly recommend.

Tessa Watson is a Music Therapist who works in higher education training students, and in supervisory and clinical practice. Tessa has supported people with learning disabilities to use music therapy and has worked alongside carers and colleagues from Dramatherapy and other disciplines for over 30 years.

Dramatherapy and Learning Disabilities

Dramatherapy and Learning Disabilities demonstrates the power of dramatherapy to help clients with learning disabilities, addressing current research, evidence-based work, and methods in the dramatherapy and learning disabilities fields.

Featuring contributions from 19 dramatherapists with a range of clients of all ages who have moderate to severe learning disabilities, this book presents ways in which dramatherapists are innovating new approaches to their work in the field. The authors demonstrate their expertise but also acknowledge their limitations. They explore what it is like to work in multidisciplinary teams and with parents and carers of children and adults with learning disabilities. Each chapter provides detailed vignettes of client/therapist experience and enables the reader to gain insight into therapists' thinking and the process that guides their clinical judgement. Structured accounts of sessions and outcomes, tracking clients' progress and the use of evaluation tools evidence the effectivity of dramatherapy and creative therapies' practice.

This book will be a significant resource for trainee dramatherapists, arts therapists and professionals interested in incorporating creative methods into their practice. It also provides examples of burgeoning arts therapies research within the field and lays the foundations for future projects.

Helen Milward is a Drama and Movement Therapist, who has worked with vulnerable, disadvantaged and disabled children and young people in various settings. She has managed teams of therapists both in special education and for the NHS and is currently developing a service for birthing people experiencing trauma and loss.

Anna Seymour is Emeritus Professor of Dramatherapy at the University of Roehampton London and an HCPC registered Dramatherapist.

Dramatherapy: Approaches, Relationships, Critical Ideas
Series Editor: Professor Anna Seymour

This series brings together leading practitioners and researchers in the field of Dramatherapy to explore the practices, thinking and evidence base for Dramatherapy.

Each volume focuses on a particular aspect of Dramatherapy practice, its application with a specific client group, an exploration of a particular methodology or approach or the relationship between Dramatherapy and related field(s) of practice, all informed by ongoing critical analysis of existing and emergent theoretical ideas.

In each case the aim is to develop the knowledge base of Dramatherapy as a unique discipline, whilst contextualising and acknowledging its relationship with others arts and therapeutic practices.

As such the series will produce different kinds of books to encompass a spectrum of readers from trainee Dramatherapists and arts practitioners to academic researchers engaged in multidisciplinary enquiry.

The field of Dramatherapy is expanding internationally and this series aims to respond to emergent clinical and critical needs within practice based and academic settings. These settings are increasingly diverse serving complex needs and demand dynamic and incisive literature to support clinical intervention and as resources for critique.

In this series:

Dramatherapy and Autism
Edited by Deborah Haythorne and Anna Seymour

Dramatherapy *and Borderline Personality Disorder*
By Nicky Morris

Dramatherapy with Elders and People with Dementia
By Joanna Jaaniste

Dramatherapy and Learning Disabilities
Developing Emotional Growth, Autonomy and Self-Worth
Edited by Helen Milward and Anna Seymour

https://www.routledge.com/mentalhealth/series/DRAMA

Dramatherapy and Learning Disabilities

Developing Emotional Growth, Autonomy and Self-Worth

Edited by Helen Milward
and Anna Seymour

Routledge
Taylor & Francis Group

LONDON AND NEW YORK

Designed cover image: © Shutterstock

First published 2024
by Routledge
4 Park Square, Milton Park, Abingdon, Oxon OX14 4RN

and by Routledge
605 Third Avenue, New York, NY 10158

Routledge is an imprint of the Taylor & Francis Group, an informa business

British Library Cataloguing-in-Publication Data

A catalogue record for this book is available from the British Library

Library of Congress Cataloging-in-Publication Data
Names: Milward, Helen, editor. | Seymour, Anna, editor.
Title: Dramatherapy and learning disabilities: developing emotional growth, autonomy and self-worth/edited by Helen Milward and Anna Seymour.
Description: Abingdon, Oxon; New York, NY: Routledge, 2024. | Series:
Dramatherapy: approaches, relationships, critical ideas | Includes bibliographical references and index. |
Identifiers: LCCN 2023007966 (print) | LCCN 2023007967 (ebook) | ISBN 9780367550608 (hardback) | ISBN 9780367550592 (paperback) | ISBN 9781003091783 (ebook)
Subjects: LCSH: Learning disabilities—Treatmen | Drama—Therapeutic use.
Classification: LCC RJ506.L4 D73 2024 (print) | LCC RJ506.L4 (ebook) | DDC 618.92/85889—dc23/eng/20230602
LC record available at https://lccn.loc.gov/2023007966
LC ebook record available at https://lccn.loc.gov/2023007967

ISBN: 9780367550608 (hbk)
ISBN: 9780367550592 (pbk)
ISBN 9781003091783 (ebk)

DOI: 10.4324/9781003091783

Typeset in Times New Roman
by Codemantra

This book is dedicated to Rebecca Blake.
Becky sadly passed away before we completed this
book. She left a great imprint on the world and those
who were lucky enough to have known her will always
remember her energy, enthusiasm and dedication to
those she worked with. It is an honour to be able to
hold a piece of her legacy within this book and that her
work will live on in these pages.

Contents

Contributors

Melanie Beer is a Sesame trained drama and movement therapist and clinical supervisor (CAST). She works in the NHS and has a private practice. Alongside her work with Adults with Learning Disabilities, Melanie has practiced with many different client groups and has significant experience in working in forensic mental health. Melanie has experienced gestalt psychotherapy for many years, as part of her personal growth and development and has been inspired to attend trainings and CPD within this area. She runs regular CPD events on themes including emotional abuse and coercive control, narcissism, trauma and attachment. Melanie is a regional representative for the British Association for Dramatherapists for Wales and has co-created many conferences in Wales as part of Dramatherapy Wales/ Dramatherapi Cymru. Like Gillian Downie, she is also a member of the Golden Thread Playback Theatre Company.

Rebecca Blake qualified as a dramatherapist on the Dramatherapy MA at Roehampton University where she subsequently became a Senior Lecturer. She worked as a Specialist Arts Therapist in a large Arts Therapy team within an academy of SEN schools. Her clinical experience included mainstream education (primary and secondary), Child and Adolescent Mental Health, as a CAMHS Practitioner, adult and older adult acute mental health, adult alcohol and drug services, prisons, home office and domestic violence charities. Rebecca trained as an actress at the Webber Douglas Academy of Dramatic Art resulting in a 15-year career in both television and theatre.

Jane Bourne is a senior Arts Psychotherapist (Dramatherapist) at Cumbria, Northumberland, Tyne and Wear NHS Foundation Trust. She has worked within inpatient Specialist Services with vulnerable adults who have a learning disability and mental health difficulties as well as young people and adolescents. Her work has included implementing a community pathway using dramatherapy groups with a focus on preventing re-admissions and enabling post-discharge support. Her Trust awarded these groups with a service user involvement 'Shining a Light' award. Jane is currently the Chair of the British Association of Dramatherapists and has won a number of research awards from Health Education

England's National Institute of Research, including an Internship, a Clinical Research Masters and a Green shoots award.

Rosalind Davidson qualified as a dramatherapist at Roehampton University in 2013. The Hero's Journey is an integral part of the syllabus at Roehampton and had a huge impact on her own process. She felt that the understanding and assimilation of its potential application with young people with learning disabilities and the depth of process allowed for real potential to facilitate transformation. Since qualifying she has worked for a number of years in education settings with children and young people with MLD, Autism and ADHD who have experienced trauma or Adverse Childhood Experiences (ACEs).

Rosalind published in *Dramatherapy and Autism* (2017) her chapter, 'Entering Colourland: Working with Metaphor with High Functioning Autistic Children' and used case study vignettes to counter the presumption that Autistic people can't work in metaphor and to demonstrate the effectiveness of Dramatherapy in working with this client group.

Gillian Downie is a Sesame drama and movement therapist, supervisor (CAST) and Gestalt Psychotherapist. She works in the NHS and has a private practice. For many years she belonged to a dialogic group run by Anne Pettit, thus experiencing personally the power of presence and confirmation. With Martin Capps, she facilitates ongoing experiential groups to explore shame in the therapeutic relationship. She has been the Co-Convenor and is now a Guest Trainer on Mary Smail's Psyche and Soma Sesame Training. She is also a guest trainer at Gestalt Centre Wales. Gillian runs regular CPD events on themes including personality adaptations, white privilege, coercive control, and attachment. Gillian is part of the Golden Thread Playback Theatre Company, who have been performing together for the past nine years. This work has included co-performing with adults with learning disabilities. She facilitates several supervision groups which use the ritual of playback forms to facilitate new perspectives in therapeutic relationships.

Jessie Ellinor is a qualified Drama and Movement Therapist and Creative Arts Supervisor who holds a Postgraduate Certificate in Childhood Bereavement and a Foundation in Group Analysis. She specialises in working with children, young people, families and staff in education. In her private practice, she supervises therapists/counsellors, staff in education and children's hospices. She has published work on play, family work, disability, transitions and collaboration across arts therapy modalities. Jessie is the co-author of *Hugo's Hops* (2022), a children's book about disability.

Jessie has played an active role as a visiting lecturer on MA Dramatherapy trainings and has facilitated workshops in the UK and abroad. She is a previous member of BADTh's Supervision Sub-committee and is a former co-chair of the Creative Arts Supervision Forum.

Jessie is an ardent advocate of the healing power of play. This inspired her to create Facing Feelings (www.facingfeelings.co.uk), a series of games that therapeutically encourage the sharing of emotions. Jessie is currently co-creating a 'playful platform' for therapists and clients working online: www.therapyfairground.org

Amee Freyone graduated from the Drama & Movement Therapy (Sesame) MA course at the Royal Central School of Speech and Drama in 2016. She spent ten years working with children and young people with learning disabilities/additional needs before training as a Dramatherapist and returned to this field of work once she was qualified. Amee spent three years in full-time clinical work in special needs education but has also worked in a residential dementia care setting, a drug and alcohol treatment and recovery centre, and in schools for children with social, emotional and attachment difficulties, challenging behaviour and complex needs. Amee is now working as a Dramatherapist in schools in Gibraltar.

Tim Goldman is a trained dramatherapist, teacher and actor. Tim's work is primarily in schools, where he is currently providing one-to-one sessions for primary aged children who have suffered trauma. Tim also uses a version of Cognitive Behavioural therapy combined with the Dramatherapy to help children with acute anxiety or low mood. Previous to this, much of Tim's therapy work was providing group therapy sessions in SEN schools for children with profound and multiple learning difficulties, as well as facilitating dramatherapy sessions for older people with dementia and a range of other learning disabilities. Tim also runs workshops in creative movement and play for all ages. These use various drama techniques including improvisation and clowning. He is currently delivering this in a horticultural environment for people of all ages and abilities.

Simon Hackett is a Consultant Arts Psychotherapist at Cumbria, Northumberland, Tyne and Wear NHS Foundation Trust, he holds an HEE/NIHR (Health Education England/National Institute for Health Research) Integrated Clinical-Academic programme, Senior Clinical Lectureship Fellowship, and is a Senior Clinical Lecturer in Mental Health at the Population Health Sciences Institute, Newcastle University. Simon has a track record in designing and delivering funded research on the arts psychotherapies (art, music, drama, dance therapy). His research interests and experience include developing and evaluating complex interventions and clinical trials focusing on improving mental health, wellbeing and recovery.

Seren Haf Grime worked part time in the NHS for ten years in Mental Health and Learning Disability Directorates and part time in schools. She now works in the Head Office at Chroma Therapies where she continues to offer supervision, reflective groups, formulation sessions and training. She is a visiting lecturer at the University of South Wales MA Art Psychotherapy course which includes facilitating Experiential Reflective Groups and Group Supervision. She enjoys facilitating joint modality individual sessions and groups with arts therapists, psychologists and nurses. She is trained in Positive Behavioural Support and integrates more psychodynamic views into a behavioural model. She has completed Dialectical Behaviour Therapy training and Compassion Focused Therapy training, attended Therapeutic Writing courses with Metanoia Institute and is a Playback Theatre practitioner.

Seren is a co-founder of Creative Therapies Collective which sources funding to enable the arts therapies to be accessible to all across South Wales.

Lina Ib came to value the therapeutic benefits of play and creativity whilst working with children with an ASD diagnosis as a Psychology undergraduate. This led to her training as a drama and movement therapist. Since qualifying in 2005, she has continued to work consistently with children and young people, both in mainstream and specialist education as well as privately. She also worked for Women's Aid for many years supporting children and their mothers who had experienced domestic abuse. In addition, she has extensive experience of working with adults with moderate to severe learning disabilities. Initially in an NHS setting and then in day centres, both in group and individual sessions. She has also worked with older adults with dementia. She is currently supporting children in mainstream schools who have suffered complex developmental trauma.

Amy Keenan is qualified in Drama and Movement Therapy. Since qualifying and using her skills from a care background, Amy has been a full-time Dramatherapist for a children's hospice working with children, young people and their families with life-limiting, life-threatening conditions, and palliative care- working within the community and at the residential unit. She conducts in-house training and has regularly co-facilitated with other therapists as well as liaising with other organisations and professionals. Amy has recently started working as a CAMHS Clinical Professional and qualified as an EMDR therapist in March 2022. She also has a small private practice specialising in children with SEN and EBD, working within private and community-based teams.

Georgina Harris completed her BMus in performance at the Royal College of Music in 2012 and spent the first six years of her career working as a freelance viola player: performing, teaching, recording and leading interactive workshops. She decided to specialise in Music Therapy and completed her Masters at Roehampton University in 2019. Georgie now works as a Music Therapist for The Eden Academy and is a member of their Creative Arts Therapy team, delivering individual and group Music Therapy for children and teenagers with additional needs. She also works for the King's Cross based charity, 'Growing Hope', providing short-term Music Therapy interventions for children with additional needs and their parents. As well as working in education, she also has experience working within neuro-disability rehabilitation and has a passion for using music to enable growth and development for all, no matter their age or ability.

Helen Milward is a Sesame trained Drama and Movement Therapist. She worked with vulnerable, disadvantaged and disabled children and young people for 14 years in various settings, including 12 years as the Arts Therapy Service Manager at the Eden Academy Trust of special schools. Helen has presented and run workshops at a number of conferences and events, both within the dramatherapy community and across care and education settings. She has guided the development of strong multi-professional approaches, operating across a variety of services and provisions; this has also led to external consultation on institutional developments, service structure and documentation. Helen has undertaken research and jointly established evaluation tools with learning disability client groups. Helen is a Creative Arts Supervisor and supervises a range of professionals and students as well as offering training to those working with the arts in community settings. Helen is currently setting up a new NHS service for birthing people experiencing trauma and loss.

Amanda Musicka-Williams completed her Masters in Drama and Movement Therapy at the Central School of Speech and Drama in 2004. She has practiced in both Australia and the United Kingdom. Amanda is passionate about working with young people with intellectual/developmental disabilities. Her PhD was completed in 2020. In both that and more recent research, Amanda has explored the intersection between dramatherapy and personal learning, with a view to expanding accessible and creative teaching processes in special education, where she has worked as a Dramatherapist for 17 years. Other areas of work include community mental health, forensic, alternative and mainstream education, domestic violence support and homeless services. Amanda teaches on the Masters of Creative Arts Therapies at the University of Melbourne, training both Dramatherapists and Dance Movement Therapists.

Jennifer Pullan completed training at Roehampton University in 2017 and has worked for the NHS periodically for 12 years, in London and surrounding areas; Jen has been successful in the creation and development of a Dramatherapist role within a forensic low secure learning disability service in the South East of England. Dramatherapy has since expanded across this service which now hosts a growing arts therapies team. Jen has a particular interest in the development of an arts therapies patient reported outcome measure (PROM), specific to forensics and learning disabilities.

Previous experience includes voluntary work for Mencap with adults with learning disabilities and 6 years as a part time support worker for children with mild to severe learning disabilities.

Sophie Riga de Spinoza is a qualified Music Therapist and Integrative Psychotherapist and plays the piano, guitar, clarinet and saxophone. Since graduating, Sophie has worked consistently as a Music therapist in education with children and young people across a wide range of special needs and abilities. She is passionate about making music an accessible therapeutic medium for all and works as a practitioner with The Amber Trust, working musically to support families with visually impaired and blind pre-school aged children.

Sophie has facilitated a number of education, music therapy and supervision workshops, most recently at the British Association for Music Therapy 2021 Conference, where she delivered a presentation on supporting staff in the workplace. She is a Creative Arts Supervisor and provides supervision for students and staff at her workplace, as well as arts therapists in her own private practice. She is currently a visiting lecturer on the Creative Arts Supervision Training Diploma.

Luke Simonds spent the first 14 years of his career working in learning and development for both the public and private sectors. He has been working in education for ten years. As a teacher, Luke has worked with children and young adults aged 4–19, in mainstream and special education settings. As a Dramatherapist, Luke has facilitated individual and group Dramatherapy interventions for children, young adults and older people with Social, Emotional and Mental Health needs in both education and health settings. Luke currently works as an Assistant Head Teacher and Dramatherapist at a school for children with Severe Learning Difficulties. In addition, Luke is a member of the board of directors for NESSie In Ed CIC, a mental health service which provides art therapies and counselling to children and young people in educational settings across Hertfordshire and Essex. Luke lives and works in Hertfordshire.

Hayley Southern is a Dramatherapist and qualified in EMDR. She is the Co-convenor of the British Association of Dramatherapists' (BADth) Inclusion & Visibility Subcommittee, as well as Lead for the Disability & Illness Matters Working Group. Hayley has a private practice at Southern Compass and has worked with a wide range of ages and client groups, including adoption, addiction, forensics, education, SEMH, LGBTQ+ and people with physical and learning disabilities, as well as life-threatening and limiting illnesses. She regularly provides consultations and training sessions for various organisations. Hayley co-presented the Keynote on 'Psychological Trauma & Resilience' at BADth's 2019 Annual Conference. She contributed a clinical commentary to the special LGBTQ+ issue of the Dramatherapy Journal and is a guest co-editor (with Mary Smail) for the 2023 'Dramatherapists with Disabilities & Illnesses' special issue. This will be the theme of BADth's 2023 annual conference for which Hayley will act as co-convenor.

Introduction

Helen Milward

Introduction

> A learning disability is a reduced intellectual ability and difficulty with every-
> day activities [...] People with a learning disability tend to take longer to learn
> and may need support to develop new skills, understand complicated informa-
> tion and interact with other people.
>
> (Mencap 2021)

Following the success in this series of *Dramatherapy and Autism* (Haythorne &
Seymour 2017) and *Dramatherapy for Borderline Personality Disorder* (Morris
2018), the present book aims to provide readers the experience, knowledge and
research into current practice of dramatherapists, whose clients have learning
disabilities.

In my own research and discussions with arts therapists, it became clear that
there is a need for literature which looks at the issues that people with learning
disabilities are facing and for more documentation of what dramatherapy can offer
this client group in changing times. This book will examine current and developing
practices and methods in using dramatherapy with both children and adults with
learning disabilities. It addresses how the understanding of, and approaches to,
those with learning disabilities continue to change, questioning previous expectations of the potential achievements of this client group, what gaps there are in the
understanding of their emotional development and, in particular, what the role of
the dramatherapist might be in relation to these issues.

Over the years, there have been many shifts in the way people with learning
disabilities have been thought about, not just in the therapeutic community but
throughout society. It was not long ago that people with a wide range of disabilities were largely locked away from society. Little was expected from them, and
there was an assumption that they would have a lifelong need of dependency. They
faced institutional 'infantilisation' and were often sent to live in hospitals and care
homes.

Research into attitudes towards people with disabilities has revealed the struggles they have faced historically. The NHS North West's Equality, Inclusion and

DOI: 10.4324/9781003091783-1

Human Rights Team (Grant 2013) quotes Aristotle as having said that blind people 'become senseless and incapable of reason'. Grant recounts that in the 1400s, medical texts portrayed 'lunatics, as well as other disabled people, [...] as unkempt, frenzied and dishevelled', while a medieval King's jester or fool would likely have been someone with a learning disability. She outlines the use of institutions throughout the 19th and early 20th centuries and cites The Mental Deficiency Act of 1913, which 'categorises people with learning disabilities and mental health issues as "idiots", "imbeciles", "feeble-minded" or "moral defectives"' (Grant 2013).

History has seen persecution, 'mercy killings' and discriminative laws as recently as the mid-1900s. Social attitudes to those with learning disabilities often resulted in avoidance being the key issue driving legislation. Shame led to people being 'hidden' from society. Cultural connotations, which continue in some parts of the world today, suggested that parents were being 'punished' for their wrongdoings by having a disabled child, or that a child was possessed by an evil spirit or by witchcraft. It is only comparatively recent that discrimination against people with disabilities has been outlawed (UK Public General Acts 2010).

Thankfully, due to the hard work of campaigners and research and literature produced by practitioners working with people with learning disabilities, significant shifts have occurred in societal thinking. Interventions and practices addressing learning disabilities are expanding, and research into individual developments has led to an increased expectation of what people with learning disabilities can achieve. Education and employment opportunities have grown significantly, as well as the possibility for people to make 'life choices', with a focus on 'age appropriate' interventions and individualised provision.

This book is structured chronologically by the age of the client groups, comprises contributors' encounters with people with differing learning disabilities and examines examples of the challenges and successes throughout their lives.

In Part 1, **Special Educational and Needs and Disabilities**, Jessie Ellinor and Sophie Riga de Spinoza explore family dynamics when a new sibling arrives in Chapter 2 which follows the experiences of one client and his family in the setting of a Special School, describing the interventions the school created to help with this life transition. In Chapter 3, Luke Simonds asks the question: 'May we speak for you?' and addresses the challenges of advocating for children with profound and multiple learning difficulties (PMLD) in an educational setting – the assumptions that professionals make – and finding a way for the clients to have a 'voice'. Helen Milward's Chapter 4 summarises research in applying an evaluation tool to the tracking of social and emotional development in children and young people in a Special Educational Needs and Disabilities (SEND) setting.

Part 2, **The Journey Through Adolescence**, addresses clients who continue to struggle with their disabilities, at the same time as going through the turmoil of adolescence. Amee Freyone's case study, in Chapter 5, describes an intervention with her client Maddy, using the concept of the 'therapy space' in order to work through client anxiety and build a relationship prior to 'getting to' the space. Chapter 6 details a case study in which Rosalind Davidson takes the reader through the process that she and her client undertook with the monomyth of 'The Hero's Journey', in which, by using the 'distancing of story', the dramatherapist helped her client find creativity and begin to understand their life experiences. Similarly, in Chapter 7, Hayley Southern uses a case study to explore her client's journey of 'Finding the Self' in his transition to adulthood. Amanda Musicka-Williams' Chapter 8 draws attention to the processes of imitative learning and flexibility, through her doctoral research examining group dramatherapy with adolescents in special education.

Part 3, **On to Adulthood**, contributors focus on the challenges of wanting to be independent adults while still needing support in order to achieve this. Melanie Beer and Gillian Downie address the theme of shame for adults with learning disabilities in Chapter 9, describing how dramatherapy provides a valuable opportunity to offer confirmation to the individual, by acknowledging their unique personalities alongside their disabilities. In Chapter 10, Tim Goldman and Lina Ib provide vignettes from a year-long group for adults with moderate learning disabilities. They highlight the importance of attunement and attachment in creating essential developmental opportunities, through co-facilitation. Seren Haf Grime's Chapter 11 describes the benefits of working closely within a multi-professional team, which enabled a holistic, multilayered approach and understanding of service users' needs. Jen Pullan's exploration of developing a dramatherapy service in a forensic, low-secure unit, in Chapter 12, sees the use of creative approaches, such as masks and stories, to increase emotional understanding and a better sense of self. The chapter reveals the complexities of learning disabilities combined with mental health difficulties.

Part 4, **Coping with Change**, highlights the challenges for people with learning disabilities at different ages when confronted with change and major life events. In Chapter 13, Jane Bourne and Dr Simon Hackett discuss the success of their 'Get Going Group', which has enabled participants to manage their discharge from hospital and *becoming* part of a wider community. Jessie Ellinor and Amy Keenan 'make connections through life and death' in Chapter 14, in which they explore the complexities of preparing for, and coping with death. This chapter considers the experiences of death in two contexts: a SEND setting, in which deaths of pupils, family members and staff need to be addressed and a hospice for children with life-limiting and life-threatening diagnoses. Chapter 15 tackles more recent challenges to arts therapists working with clients with learning disabilities, during the Covid-19 pandemic. Rebecca Blake and Georgina Harris outline their experiences of trying to be adaptable, creative and flexible during the Covid lockdown. They include the experiences of others, within their service and elsewhere, in relation to challenges and positive aspects of this change in ways of offering dramatherapy.

The chapters in this book combine their collective evidence to demonstrate the effectivity of dramatherapy. Although faced with the many challenges of functioning in mainstream society – coping with issues such as shame, confusion, lack of autonomy and vulnerability, dramatherapy assists these clients to access learning, develop self-awareness and discover their own creative potential. Thus, as Rosalind Davidson asserts in her chapter, Dramatherapy gives these clients a

> space in which to reflect on how [they feel]. It is through being the leader of their own therapeutic process, and by expressing their 'voices', that those with learning disabilities can be supported to have agency in their own lives.

Consent for publication has been obtained from clients, parents, carers and professionals involved in the work described here. In accordance with HCPC's standards of conduct, performance and ethics, relevant codes of practice have been observed in relation to respecting client confidentiality.

References

Grant, L. ed. 2013. *A Disability History Timeline: The Struggle for Equal Rights through the Ages*. NHS North West's Equality, Inclusion and Human Rights team. https://ukdhm.org/v2/wp-content/uploads/2014/09/B5-Disability-Time-Line-NHS-North-West.pdf Accessed: 14 October 2021.

Haythorne, D. & Seymour, A. 2017. *Dramatherapy and Autism*. London and New York. Routledge, Taylor and Francis.

Mencap. 2021. *What is a Learning Disability*. https://www.mencap.org.uk/learning-disability-explained/what-learning-disability Accessed: 14 October 2021.

Morris, N. 2018. *Dramatherapy for Borderline Personality Disorder: Empowering and Nurturing People through Creativity*. London and New York. Routledge, Taylor and Francis.

UK Public General Acts. 2010. *Equality Act 2010*. https://www.legislation.gov.uk/ukpga/2010/15/contents Accessed: 14 October 2021.

Chapter 1

Dramatherapy and Learning Disabilities

Helen Milward

If we have learnt anything from recent times, with lockdown, global pandemic, and societal uncertainty, it is that dramatherapy remains consistently in a state of 'flux' (Jones 2021). The need to be flexible within our boundaries is more prevalent than ever. Notwithstanding the constant changes that we therapists and our clients face, society has been challenged in unprecedented ways in the response to COVID-19. Despite the upheaval, many dramatherapists have continued to evolve how and what is offered and taken up the challenge of creating consistency for clients; change, flexibility, and adaptation is nothing new to the discipline of dramatherapy.

Dramatherapists have worked with clients with learning disabilities as a crucial intervention, since the mid-1900s. This work not only offers the client group many benefits, but working with these clients has influenced and aided the development of dramatherapy itself. This book explores a variety of ways in which current practitioners are engaging with children and adults with learning disabilities and are continuing to develop new methods and undertake research in the field.

Learning Disabilities: Definitions and Diagnosis

A common definition of a learning disability is 'a reduced intellectual ability and difficulty with everyday activities' (Mencap 2019). As with any diagnosed disability, there is a wide spectrum which encompasses the impact that having a learning disability has on an individual, it ranges from mild, moderate (MLD), severe (SLD), and profound and multiple learning disabilities (PMLD). It is, therefore, hard to reach a specific definition that encapsulates all the nuances and variances in ability of this client group.

Individuals can be diagnosed as having MLD, SLD, or PMLD, but more common is an additional diagnosis of a condition associated with learning disabilities, such as Down's syndrome, global developmental delay, cerebral palsy, Williams syndrome, and fragile X syndrome.

Learning disabilities are essentially caused by an impact on the early development of the central nervous system. This may occur in the womb, by the mother having an accident or illness, or through the effect of certain genes. A baby's brain

DOI: 10.4324/9781003091783-2

development can be affected during childbirth by lack of oxygen, trauma to the head, or being premature. Post-birth learning disabilities can occur because of early childhood illness, accidents, or seizures. Due to the range of impacts on brain development, a diagnosis might be made before or after birth but may not be identified until later stages of development.

The World Health Organisation (WHO) describes the diagnoses of disability

as an umbrella term for impairments, activity limitations and participation restrictions. Disability is the interaction between individuals with a health condition (e.g. cerebral palsy, Downs syndrome and depression) and personal and environmental factors (e.g. negative attitudes, inaccessible transportation and public buildings, and limited social supports).

(WHO 2018)

The government document, *Valuing People: A New Strategy for Learning Disability for the 21st Century,* published in 2001 states:

Learning disability includes the presence of:

- A significantly reduced ability to understand new or complex information, to learn new skills (impaired intelligence) with;
- A reduced ability to cope independently (impaired social functioning);
- which started before adulthood, having a lasting effect on development. (Gov uk 2001)

The emphasis in these definitions is primarily on impairment and the lack of ability. Is this important in clarifying a diagnosis? Perhaps. However, the *Valuing People* document 'is based on the premise that people with learning disabilities are people first. We focus throughout on what people can do, with support where necessary, rather than on what they cannot do' (Gov.uk 2001). This positive attitude is the basis of this book, in which dramatherapists value highly individuals in their own space and work with the creative 'healthy' parts of the self in a collaborative process of development and healing. We should also recognise that a learning disability is an integral part of the person, their character, and their life. It is not an illness that can be cured, so the whole person needs to be addressed, as we all should be, with all our similarities and differences celebrated.

It is important to listen to the voices of those who live with a learning disability, and I therefore encourage the reader to visit the Mencap website to watch the videos of interviews with young people, adults, and their families. Some comments there that struck me were:

I've got a learning disability but it does not mean that we cannot work just as well as anybody else. Sometimes we can do the job even better.

(Mencap 2019)

A learning disability means slowing down and appreciating just the smaller things in life, the smaller achievements that our little boy can do, that maybe other people take for granted.

(Mencap 2016)

A learning disability should not be used as a label. Every person is different, whether they have a learning disability or not.

(Mencap 2015)

Attitudes to Learning Disabilities

As dramatherapists, a client's diagnosis informs our preparation, approach, and use of practical resources, but ultimately, our focus must be on the person present within the session, on how we not only promote their relational and emotional abilities but also their sense of self.

The journey to self-discovery for those with learning disabilities is tainted by a history of cultural perceptions, attitudes, and prejudice, as Tony Blair writes in the foreword to the 'Valuing People' document:

People with learning disabilities can lead full and rewarding lives as many already do. But others find themselves pushed to the margins of our society. And almost all encounter prejudice, bullying, insensitive treatment and discrimination at some time in their lives. Such prejudice and discrimination – no less hurtful for often being unintentional – has a very damaging impact. It leads to your world becoming smaller, opportunities more limited, a withdrawal from wider society so time is spent only with family, carers or other people with learning disabilities.

(Gov.uk 2001)

Referencing David O'Driscoll's writing about learning disabilities, Tamsin Cottis comments that a

subtle over identification with learning disability may have led some of the early twentieth-century pioneers to hide their work from public view, in much the same way as families have sought to hide their disabled child from the glare of the community.

(Cottis 2009, 23)

Prejudice and misunderstanding have led to a history of labelling those with learning disabilities as 'abnormal' thus re-enforcing their – and their family's – feelings of shame and isolation. There is still a need for a wider understanding of the abilities of people with learning disabilities. However, the way we think and talk about disabilities has been shifted by research into this client group, as published in journals such as *British Journal of Learning Disabilities*, *Learning Disability Quarterly*, and *Learning Disabilities: A Multidisciplinary Journal.*

Research into Learning Disabilities

Notable research into the social and emotional development of people with learning disabilities includes William N. Bender's study of students with learning disabilities. He looked at their social-emotional development through the mid-1990s, as well as addressing the risk for adolescents experiencing depression and suicide (Bender & Wall 1994; Huntington & Bender 1993).

Earlier research, while recognising the link between learning disabilities and 'social disabilities', referred to studies in the field of neurology, such as the work of Denckla (1983) and Weintraub and Mesulam (1983), both of which explore the impact of 'developmental disorders' (Denckla 1983) and how they 'may lead to chronic emotional difficulties, a disturbance of interpersonal skills, and poor visuospatial ability' (Weintraub & Mesulam 1983).

Yet, despite this research, Andrew R. Arthur's article, *The Emotional Lives of People with Learning Disability* (Arthur 2003), states that it is still a 'much neglected' area and confirms my concern that there is very little research that addresses the high level of emotional developmental problems for those with learning disabilities. Arthur's study into parent–infant bonding, child development psychological assessment, and emotional disturbance advocated the need for 'multidisciplinary attention if progress in improving quality of life is to be maintained' (Arthur 2003).

Across four editions of her book, *Learning about Learning Disabilities*, Bernice Wong (Wong & Butler 2012) develops her research on the resilience of people with learning disabilities and the extent of individuals' self-awareness of the nature of their own disability. She describes 'successful adults' as being able to compartmentalise their disability as one aspect of their identity. She describes them as 'proactive', believing they have the power to control the direction of their lives, being extremely persistent, flexible, able to set realistic goals, and take advantage of opportunity. However, she also notes that 'almost all of the adults with learning disabilities described experiencing stress and exhaustion as a result of their learning disability that, at times caused depressive symptoms and high levels of anxiety' (Wong & Butler 2012).

The challenge of acknowledging a disability reminds me of Valerie Sinason's description of the courage it takes to not 'conform' to the 'handicapped smile'.

> Opening your eyes to admitting you look, sound, walk, talk, move or think differently from the ordinary, average person, let alone a cult hero or heroine, takes greater reserves of courage, honesty and toleration of one's own envy. It can be easier to behave like the village idiot and make everyone laugh than to expose the unbearable tiny discrepancy between normal and not normal on the human continuum.
>
> (Sinason 1992, 21)

Throughout my work as a dramatherapist, I am continually frustrated when clients in my sessions 'choose' the 'happy' symbol when asked to reflect how they are. This is not a frustration with the clients themselves, but with a system that has taught them that they are expected to be happy, a society that has influenced them to be compliant and conform in order to be 'likeable', rather than express a true representation of who they are in that moment. Reflecting on this, however, I also recall an early experience of working with adults with learning disabilities prior to my training as a dramatherapist. In 2005, Bournemouth Theatre in Education Company facilitated a group of adults with learning disabilities to create a play about their experiences of being bullied. They then performed around local mainstream schools and facilitated a workshop for the pupils to further address issues of bullying. The courage and honesty of this group to share their experiences was inspirational. They accepted their disabilities but not any limitations on harnessing their talents and so were able to promote changing perceptions.

Thomas and Wood, a teacher and a social worker, write about finding the balance between two fields of existing writing: developing theoretical perspectives and actual work with people with learning disabilities themselves on various aspects of their life. They draw upon Neil Thompson's *Anti-discriminatory Practice* (1997) in their work on promoting empowerment, commenting that Thompson 'suggests that this is achievable through the use of person-centred work, by developing the confidence of the individual and through the use of advocacy to help reinforce the right to inclusion and equality within society' (Thomas & Wood 2003, 114). The concept of 'person-centred' work provides a good point to link theories about learning disability to those of dramatherapy. The client-led nature of our interventions makes a significant contribution in this field.

Dramatherapy in the Field of Learning Disability

To avoid repetition, in providing a clear definition of dramatherapy itself, I refer the reader to other books in this series, *Dramatherapy and Autism* (Haythorne & Seymour 2016) and *Dramatherapy for Borderline Personality Disorder* (Morris 2018). They both draw attention to the definition on the British Association of Dramatherapy website (BADth 2022) and highlight drama as 'an implicit function within human development and as part of a metaphorical vocabulary through which human beings express their thoughts and feelings' (Haythorne & Seymour 2016). These books also explore the historical development of drama as therapy and name theatre practitioners such as Augusto Boal whose work 'resonates with the dramatherapy process, such as the notion that true liberation from oppression may be rehearsed through a shared dramatic experience' (Morris 2018).

However, rather than just *addressing* '**What** is dramatherapy?', the aim of this book is to answer the more specific question: 'What can dramatherapy **do** for those with learning disabilities?' As a brief answer, I offer you a list of benefits, as it provides a place and opportunity:

- to simply be yourself and to have freedom to play
- to explore and develop a greater sense of self, discovering who you can be and achieving autonomy
- to explore the unknown, safely and within boundaries
- to develop relationships through consistent interactions with a therapist, who offers a secure base with no expectations but with acceptance and unconditional positive regard
- to build self-esteem and confidence to find their own 'voice' to be able to speak for themselves or be advocated for

These themes, and many more, will reappear and weave their way throughout the book, highlighting the essence of what we try to offer this client group, and what the clients seem to achieve, when distanced from a world of too high or too few expectations.

Influences

Dramatherapy has developed its methods and techniques from its roots in theatre practice. Theatre practitioners have helped shape how we engage with clients through the art form; drama being the core of what we do. For example, Jerzy Grotowski's method of the actor's 'whole self' being immersed into the character, informing how we, as therapists, engage both physically and mentally with our clients. Augusto Boal's Forum Theatre of integrating the stories and imagination of the audience has helped develop how dramatherapists use stories with clients, being able to improvise and adapt in client-led sessions. We have learnt from Antonin Artaud's Theatre of Cruelty, which focuses on the relationship between actor and audience, by developing two-way interactions between therapist and client.

As a form of psychotherapy, dramatherapy is embedded and establishes its intent in the foundational writings of Sigmund Freud, Carl Jung, Irvin Yalom, and Melanie Klein. There is a rich tapestry of scholarship and practice that we as dramatherapists draw on: research into human development and neuroscience; writings on developmental stages and patterns, such as Erik Erikson's Stages of Psychosocial Development (Erikson 1998); John Bowlby's Attachment Theory(Bowlby 1988); the exploration of the 'good enough mother' and the impact of environmental factors in early childhood in Donald Winnicott's work (Winnicott 1971); and Peter Slade's (Slade 1954) examination of how children play and engage in drama.

Particular dramatherapy traditions in training influence and inform a therapist's practice, as is evidenced throughout this book, although, through practice and experience, a dramatherapist will develop their own unique style. The chapters in this book highlight the importance of being able to work closely with other practitioners, to share the languages of psychotherapy and other related areas of practice, skills, experiences, and knowledge of the client group and the individual.

Many dramatherapists have also been influenced by the work of Audrey Wethered that brings dance and movement into dramatherapy work, explaining that

> the body is the instrument it [...] enables [the client] to relate and adapt to other people [...] not only is the whole body involved but that there is thought and feeling, sensation and imagination behind even that small action.
>
> (Wethered 1993, 18)

Similarly, Veronica Sherborne's *Developmental Movement for Children* (2001) has also been influential. Sherborne documents the importance for children, especially those with special needs, to have a sense of their own bodies. She explores how they move, what different parts of their bodies can do and how they

> experience the trunk, the centre of the body and the link between the extremities, in many of the relationship-play activities. [...] This helps the child to develop a sense of wholeness, and an awareness that parts of the body are well connected to each other.
>
> (Sherborne 2001, 4)

The influence of other practitioners such as Dave Hewett's *Intensive Interaction* (Hewett & Firth 2011), referred to in this book, and Flo Longhorn's *Sensory Drama for Very Special People* (2000) continues to influence and help adapt our practice.

A Brief History of Dramatherapy and Learning Disabilities

In the 1970s, important legislation established the rights to equality for disabled people. The UK was one of the first in the world to address these rights in the *Chronically Sick and Disabled Persons Act* (Grant 2013). At the same time, dramatherapy was expanding its work with people with learning disabilities. Through working with institutionalised people in the early 1970s, as part of the *KATS Mime and Movement Group*, Marian Lindkvist bore witness to the impact of interactive theatre with vulnerable people (Lindkvist 1998). She combined her own ideas from this group work with the evolving and established research of other practitioners and theorists, to develop the Sesame Approach to drama and movement therapy: exploring ways to engage through movement, non-verbal work, and by a consciously oblique approach.

This era also saw the development of Sue Jennings' work, exploring the impact of drama on the human psyche and making connections between the relatively 'new discipline' of dramatherapy and ancient healing rituals (Jennings 1987). Sue Jennings' focus on the early developmental years and her work with children has provided crucial insight. From her concept of *Remedial Drama* (Jennings 1982) to developing *Neuro-Dramatic-Play* (NDP) and *Embodiment-Projection-Role* (EPR) (Jennings 2013), therapists have been offered tools, processes, and methods to work with a variety of clients and has made a significant impact on the way drama-therapy is accessed by those with learning disabilities.

From the earliest dramatherapy trainings, students have gained experience of working with learning disabilities by using existing institutions. The charity Roundabout, founded in 1986 by Deborah Haythorne and Lynn Cedar, who are 'dedicated to transforming the lives of vulnerable people, using the creative power of dramatherapy to enhance mental health' (Roundabout 2021), used one such place: Orchard Hill, a residential community, remembered fondly by those who worked there (Benbow 2008).

In the 1990s, important studies on dramatherapy with learning disabilities noted how dramatherapy brings 'about a significant degree of growth and change' (Deane 1996, 119) and provided the 'release of such deeply held emotional tension' (James 1996, 214). Ann Cattanach's exploration of *Drama for People with Special Needs* observes that for 'adults and children who have lost the ability to be creative [...] play is the safe way to explore their possibilities' (Cattanach 1996, 20). Anna Chesner offered a significant contribution with her book *Dramatherapy for People with Learning Disabilities: A World of Difference* (1995) and her other publications on group work. Exploring the varied levels of learning disabilities alongside different aspects of dramatherapy, Chesner comments on the many unknown areas of this work, and that while we as therapists are

deeply moved by the creativity [we] witness in sessions, as well as by the content of what is expressed through one or other methods, [...] the dramatherapeutic journey happens on many levels. [...] The light is partial. Much of the journey still takes place in the dark and with a sense of shared adventure.

(Chesner 1995, 12–13)

As dramatherapy continued to develop into the 2000s, so too did writing capturing the therapist's journey with this client group. Such references include Clive Holmwood reflecting on the impact of the 'institutional' on the 'notion' of 'who I am and what I do as a therapist' (Holmwood 2000); Paula Crimmins book *Drama Therapy and Storymaking in Special Education* (2006) outlines the impact of using *story* offering story suggestions and ideas of how to use them.

Stories contain themes that are developmentally relevant [...] and mirror some of the issues in the student's life. [...] Traditional stories provide opportunities for interactive dramatic play, [...] as achievable 'tasks' that are modelled by the therapist using limited and simplified verbal instruction accompanied by encouragement.

(Crimmins 2006, 177)

Links were developed within schools through dramatherapy offering positive relationships that offered a 'different dynamic' (Christensen 2010, 87) between therapists and student to that of teacher and student, which '[encouraged] students to develop a sense of attachment to the school' (Christensen 2010, 86). Education staff were challenged to think about the feelings and experiences of those they teach 'to help make sense of the young people's behaviour' (Roger 2012, 130). Our ability to offer 'time' to clients was identified as essential for those who struggle to process information and 'having time to get their meaning across to others, and importantly, to find ways to support communication' (Powis 2010, 9). 'Any person with profound and multiple disabilities is a unique and whole human being, complex and impossible to quantify' (Booker 2011, 12). A study into using dramatherapy to develop social skills concluded 'improving communication skills is a major benefit attributed to the use of creative therapies' (Folostina et al 2015). In the exploration of a model named *The ACTing Cure*, authors describe that, 'For those whose capacity for language is often diminished, the ACTing cure through its use of playful creativity may provide an untapped resource for personal growth and healing' (Tomasula & Szucs 2015). Similarly, the 'drama offers children opportunities to experiment with different ways of engaging with others, to discover the consequences of their actions and behaviour in safety, one-step-removed' (Sherratt & Peter 2002, 64). It has also been important to highlight the significance of offering direct, systemic interventions with carers and families; providing parents with the 'opportunity to playfully interact with their child and [...] see their child interacting in playful ways with other adults' (Ellinor 2019, 12).

The Future

When considering future developments, I come back to Phil Jones reference to 'flux' (Jones 2021). Dramatherapy will never 'stand still' in its development. No matter how many years of experience a therapist has no two clients are ever the same, there will continue to be clients that stump us, that we enter the unknown with, and that challenge us and force us to question all those many theories and tools I have been listing. We need to start again in the metaphorical and sometimes physical 'empty space'. We must continually reassess our practices, to change and adapt to the 'reality' that clients bring, whether it be conceptual or real. This book explores the developments and flexibilities occurring within the current global climate, but, of course, the contributors, including myself, do not hold all the answers, and these offerings will need to be further developed to fit the clients of the future.

From my experience of working with Special Educational Needs and Disabilities (SEND), questions often arise of what value we arts therapists add to the school or classroom experience? Shouldn't therapy provisions be more 'integrated into the curriculum'? Shouldn't the development of a therapy service that addresses social, emotional, and mental health and informs individuals' education, health, and care plans become integrated within the requirements of the day-to-day teaching of *all* pupils with their varying levels of 'learning disability'?

I would like to see in the future a world where access to creative therapies is a statutory provision for all people with learning disabilities. In order to achieve this, as a collective of dramatherapists who work with this client group, we need to undertake more research, expand our theoretical frameworks, and push for and contribute to more in-depth understanding of the 'learning disability brain', to move away from referencing 'typical development' but having clarity on the many levels, variants, and environmental impacts on those with learning disabilities, in order to offer them 'better practice' across all services. We should not do this in isolation. The insight of other professionals, educators, speech and language therapists, occupational therapists, behaviour specialists, social workers, and medical professionals, not to forget the families and carers, is invaluable to these developments. They are essential in order to better understand the individuals and continue to evolve a focus on abilities rather than disability.

With a vast array of tools, skills, methods, and experience to tap into, dramatherapy has become a rich and wide-reaching resource as an intervention for people with learning disabilities to access. The chapters in this book highlight how dramatherapists continue to hold the space and the potential for growth, change, self-discovery, and developing relationships, by engaging our unconditional positive regard for the client. Each chapter describes and provides evidence of dramatherapists' abilities to adjust, adapt, and be flexible with what they offer in response to changes beyond both client and therapist control.

Thus, I believe that dramatherapy will continue to engage with clients, services, and institutions to create further opportunities for people with learning disabilities to find avenues for self-advocacy and personal growth.

References

Arthur, A. (2003) 'The Emotional Lives of People with Learning Disability'. In: *British Journal of Learning Disabilities.* Volume 31, Issue 1, 25–30. February 26, 2003. Wiley Online Library.

Benbow, A. (2008) 'Orchard Hill – An Appreciation'. In: *Sesame Journal: Learning Disabilities.* Issue 7, 14–19. London: Sesame Institute.

Bender, W. & Wall, M. (1994) 'Social-Emotional Development of Students with Learning Disabilities'. In: *Learning Disability Quarterly.* Volume 17, Issue 4, November 1. London: Sage Journals.

Booker, M. (2011) *Developmental Drama.* London: Jessica Kingsley Publishers.

Bowlby, J. (1988) *A Secure Base.* London: Routledge.

British Association of Dramatherapists (2022) https://www.badth.org.uk/dramatherapy/what-is-dramatherapy Accessed: March 23, 2022.

Cattanach, A. (1996) *Drama for People with Special Needs.* London: A&C (Publishers) Limited.

Chesner, A. (1995) *Dramatherapy for People with Learning Disabilities: A World of Difference.* London: Jessica Kingsley Publishers.

Christensen, J. (2010) 'Making Space Inside'. In: Karkou, V. (Ed.), *Arts Therapies in Schools: Research and Practice.* 85–96. London: Jessica Kingsley Publishers.

Cottis, T. (2009) *Intellectual Disability, Trauma and Psychotherapy*. London: Routledge.

Crimmins, P. (2006) *Dramatherapy and Storymaking in Special Education*. London: Jessica Kingsley Publisher.

Deane, M. (1996) 'Ritual in Sesame'. In: Pearson, J. (Ed.), *Discovering the Self through Drama and Movement: The Sesame Approach.* 112–120. London: Jessica Kingsley Publishers.

Denckla, M. (1983) *The Neuropsychology of Social-Emotional Learning Disabilities*. First published August 1983. New York: JAMA Neurology Journal.

Ellinor, J. (2019) 'It's the 'group' That Matters: Dramatherapy Working with a Group of Parents and Their Children Who Have Profound and Multiple Learning Difficulties'. In: *Dramatherapy Journal*. Volume 40, Issue 1, April 3, 2019. London: Sage.

Erikson, E. (1998) *The Life Cycle Completed.* London: Norton and Company.

Folostina, R., Tudorache, L., Michel, T., Erzsebet, B. & Duta, N. (2015) 'Using Drama Therapy and Storytelling in Developing Social Competences in Adults with Intellectual Disabilities of Residential Centres'. In: *Procedia: Social and Behaviour Sciences*. 1268–1274. Amsterdam: Elsevier Ltd.

Gov.uk. (2001) *Valuing People: A New Strategy for Learning Disability for the 21st Century*. https://assets.publishing.service.gov.uk/government/uploads/system/uploads/attachment_data/file/250877/5086.pdf Accessed October 10, 2020.

Grant, L. ed., (2013) *A Disability History Timeline: The Struggle for Equal Rights through the Ages.* NHS North West's Equality, Inclusion and Human Rights team: NHS. https://www.merseycare.nhs.uk/media/1749/disabiliyt-timeline-2013.pdf Accessed November 20, 2021.

Haythorne, D. & Seymour, A. (2016) *Dramatherapy and Autism.* London: Routledge.

Hewett, D. & Firth, G. (2011) *The Intensive Interaction Handbook*. London: Sage.

Holmwood, C. (2000) 'You Listen Up, Here's the Story about a Little Guy Who Lived in a Blue World…'. In: *Dramatherapy*. Volume 22, Issue 3. London: Routledge.

Huntington, D. & Bender, W. (1993) 'Adolescents with Learning Disabilities at Risk? Emotional Well-Being, Depression, Suicide'. In: *Journal of Learning Disability.* 159–166. First Published March 1, London: Sage Journals.

James, J. (1996) 'Poetry in Motion: Drama and Movement Therapy with People with Learning Disabilities'. In: Pearson, J. (Ed.), *Discovering the Self through Drama and Movement: The Sesame Approach.* 209–221. London: Jessica Kingsley Publishers.

Jennings, S. (1982) *Remedial Drama*. London: A & C Black Publishers Ltd.

Jennings, S. (1987) 'Symbolic Structures Symbolic Process'. In: *Dramatherapy*. Volume 10, Issue 2, January 1, 1987. London: Sage Journals.

Jennings, S. (2013) http://www.suejennings.com/eprndp.html Accessed September 20, 2020.

Jones, P. (2021) *The Arts Therapies: A Revolution in Healthcare,* Second Edition. London: Routledge.

Lindkvist, M. (1998) *Bring White Beads When You Call upon the Healer*. Memphis: River House Limited.

Longhorn, F. (2000) *Sensory Drama for Very Special People.* London. Catalyst Education Resources Ltd.

Mencap (2015) *What Is a Learning Disability? Mencap Young Ambassadors Tackle Stereotypes.* https://www.youtube.com/watch?v=N5I877T7RZs&feature=emb_rel_pause Accessed October 11, 2020.

Mencap (2016) *What Is a Learning Disability?* https://www.youtube.com/watch?v=tfkVA2 BKIyY Accessed October 11, 2020.

Mencap (2019) *What Is a Learning Disability?* https://www.mencap.org.uk/learning-disability-explained/what-learning-disability Accessed September 20, 2020.

Morris, N. (2018) *Dramatherapy for Borderline Personality Disorder: Empowering and Nurturing People through Creativity.* London: Routledge/Taylor and Francis.

Powis, C. (2010) 'A Dramatherapy Group with People with Learning Disabilities'. In Chislehurst, K. (Ed.), *The Prompt.* 8–9 (Winter 2010) British Association of Dramatherapy.

Roger, J. (2012) 'Learning Disabilities and Finding, Protecting and Keeping the Therapeutic Space'. In Leigh, L., Gersch, I., Dix, A. & Haythorne, D. (Eds.), *Dramatherapy with Children, Young People and Schools.* 129–136. London: Routledge.

Roundabout Website 2021: https://www.roundaboutdramatherapy.org.uk/ Accessed October 28, 2021.

Sherborne, V. (2001) *Developmental Movement for Children.* Fort Worth, TX: Derbyshire: Worth Publishing. Sherratt, D. & Peter, M. (2002) *Developing Play and Drama in children with Autistic Spectrum Disorder.* London: David Fulton Publishers.

Sinason, V. (1992) *Mental Handicap and the Human condition: New Approaches from the Taviston.* London: Free Association Books.

Slade, P. (1954) *Child Drama.* London: University of London Press Ltd.

Thomas, D. & Woods, H. (2003) *Working with People with Learning Disabilities: Theory and Practice.* London: Jessica Kingsley Publisher.

Thompson, N. (1997) *Anti-discriminatory Practice.* London: Palgrave Macmillan.

Tomasula, D. & Szucs, A. (2015) 'The ACTing Cure: Evidence-Based Group Treatment for People with Intellectual Disabilities'. In: *Dramatherapy Journal.* Volume 37, Issue 2–3. London: Sage JOURNALS.

Weintraub, S. & Mesulam, M. (1983) 'Developmental Learning Disabilities of the Right Hemisphere Emotional, Interpersonal, and Cognitive Components'. In: *JAMA Neurology Journal.* Volume 40, August 1983. New York: JAMA Neurology Journal.

Wethered, A. (1993) *Movement and Drama in Therapy: A Holistic Approach.* London: Jessica Kingsley Publishers.

WHO. (2018) *Disability and Health.* https://www.who.int/news-room/fact-sheets/detail/disability-and-health Accessed October 11, 2020.

Winnicott, D. (1971) *Playing and Reality.* London: Tavistock Publications Ltd.

Wong, B. & Butler, L. (2012) *Learning about Learning Disabilities.* Amsterdam: Elsevier Inc.

Part 1

Special Educational Needs and Disabilities

Chapter 2

Family Ties
Supporting Sibling Relationships

Jessie Ellinor and Sophie Riga de Spinoza

Introduction

When a new sibling is born, the change has a huge impact on any child's development. When the older sibling has a learning disability, the change can be felt even more acutely. The child with a disability often requires the attention of parents or carers similar to that of a child at a younger stage of development. Their needs may include having no or limited verbal language to communicate their needs, continuing intimate care (such as toileting) and/or a lack of mobility.

At a North London primary school for children with special educational needs and disabilities (SEND), where the authors work as therapists, the education staff and therapists have continually developed systems of work to ensure, where appropriate, the family (parents and siblings) are included as part of the child's learning and emotional development within school. School settings are ideally situated to support emotional growth for a child within their family context. 'School therapists take care to promote the idea that therapy […] can help all of us make sense of everyday experiences' (French & Klein 2012, 55). The child may be at their primary school from 4 to 11 years old, which allows enough time for the therapists to establish a multifaceted relationship with both the child and their family.

Sibling bonds develop, break and reform constantly throughout life. Therapeutic interventions are able to 'flex and bow' to support and grow alongside these changes, providing a confidential space where connections within the family and sibling's relationships can be explored.

This chapter presents three different interventions employed by a dramatherapist and a music therapist in a special needs school. It follows the journey of 'Adam', together with his mother, 'Jenny', and siblings 'Sienna' and 'Jake', and their engagement with each level of support offered. These were:

- A New Arrival – individual dramatherapy sessions, to prepare and support a child with learning disabilities with the birth of a new sibling
- A Shared Place to Play – group family arts therapy sessions, attended by children with learning disabilities, their parent and their preschool sibling
- Time to Be Me – therapeutic group drama/music activity days in the school holidays for mainstream siblings of children with a learning disability

DOI: 10.4324/9781003091783-4

This chapter outlines the structure and aims of the sessions offered, sharing practicalities and therapeutic rationale for how they became embedded within the school provision. It explores how providing multilayered support to the family unit of a child with a learning disability can have a significant impact on their individual lives and the life of the family as a whole. Finally, with the family's informed consent, learning from these interventions has been shared, using direct feedback from the family.

A New Arrival

The multidisciplinary team is involved with the family from early stages in their child's life. Teachers and families use a daily 'home-school' communication book. This book encourages the sharing of non-confidential information between staff, as well as through family support team meetings, annual reviews and multidisciplinary meetings. Collaborative work enables information, such as a family expecting a new baby, to be systemically held in mind. With the family's permission, the arts therapy team is notified, who then initiate interventions aimed at supporting the child's emotional well-being and understanding in this transitional period. A brief set of sessions, with either the drama or music therapist, is scheduled to coincide with the birth of the new sibling, in order to prepare the older child before and after the birth of the new baby.

This particular initiative began in 2016, when a child was referred to therapy because of a significant rise in anxiety levels and a sudden inability to emotionally regulate. These changes in behaviour were observed in class following the birth of a new sibling and subsequent changes at home. The dramatherapist provided toys and books to create a 'New Sibling' resource box, which would be accessible for staff and families to borrow, as well as for use in therapy sessions.

Case Study – Adam

Adam, a male pupil with a diagnosis of autism, was first referred to dramatherapy when he was 6 years old. The family was well known to the dramatherapist, as his older sibling, Jake, consistently accessed the Siblings Holiday sessions. On the referral form, Adam's class teacher noted that, since the arrival of his baby sister, Adam was struggling to emotionally regulate, particularly in relation to noise and unfamiliar people. He had begun to seek more physical contact from staff – possibly missing affectionate time with mum at home. The aims identified for this work, exploring themes related to the changes at home, included: support to express and regulate his emotions, to encourage vocal and non-vocal communication, and to have his own calm space to interact, play and just simply 'be'.

As Crimmens (2006) states 'The existence of an identifiable structure helps […] to tolerate and even enjoy the new, unfamiliar elements' (pg 38). Our thirty-minute dramatherapy sessions offered consistency in location and time, with ritualised beginnings and endings; hello and goodbye songs and a grounded packing-away time to de-role from the session. The central part of the session provided space for spontaneous play with relevant resources. Books, such as *The New Baby* (Civardi 2005), and toys were utilised to help contextualise the work. This included a doll with a dummy, which triggered the sound of crying when put in and out of its mouth. With the doll were other baby accessories (bath, bottle, teddy bear, nappies, clothes).

> During the initial sessions, Adam communicated that he wanted to be held or cradled by the therapist. He leant his body towards or besides the therapist initiating physical connection or reached his hands out, wanting support when balancing on 'squashy things' in the room, like the physio ball or the giant fluffy blue bear. He became increasingly aware when his movements and sounds were attuned to through 'intensive interaction', as defined by Hewett (2011); he smiled, gave sustained eye contact and repeated his communications until he got a response. Whilst the work was client led, direct phrases, such as 'we are here to think about your new brother/sister being born', were introduced by the therapist. Gradually over time, Adam became more resilient and independent. He sought less physical contact and began to interact more through play with musical instruments, objects and toys. Adam occasionally began to show an interest in the baby doll, following the dramatherapist with his gaze, as she cradled or playfully attended to it. As trust progressed, Adam began spontaneously to hold, cuddle or lie with the doll by himself. When the physical distance between Adam and the therapist was increased, his interactions became less dependent on the therapist (and with staff in Adam's classroom), allowing individual play to take place. Adam began to seem calmer, finding ways to self-regulate when anxious. Following these sessions, specially made 'new baby sibling' books were 'born' in the school. A personalised 'social story' (Gray 1993), using photographs provided by Adam's family, was organised for Adam's class and a copy was made for his family to use at home.

'New Baby Sibling' Social Story Book

'Social stories present information in a literal, "concrete" way, which may improve a person's understanding of a previously difficult or ambiguous situation or activity' (National Autistic Society 2020). Bespoke 'new baby sibling' social stories joined the pre-existing 'life-changes' templates, which were already being used in school, addressing bereavement, divorce and separation. Each book is tailored, using the child's own communication system, such as *PECS* (Picture Exchange Communication System 2020). Families often contribute photos, and sometimes actively engage their child in choosing the photos used for their book. One family sent a picture of 'mummy's tummy' with a Mickey Mouse face drawn across it. In this photograph, the child was peering at it curiously, touching his mother's pregnant tummy.

The 'new arrival' therapy sessions are designed to be a brief, focused piece of psychoeducational support. The book is ready for use in the first arts therapy session, which takes place before the new sibling is born. This allows familiar therapeutic relationships to be established prior to changes occurring at home. It enables the therapists to become 'well attuned to the child [...] to acknowledge the child's current emotional state [...] identify feelings accurately and [...] differentiate between different feeling states' (Gerhardt 2004, 51–52). Working in this way with a non-verbal child with learning disabilities, responses are given through facial gestures, sounds and movement. The therapist relies strongly on their intuition to gauge whether to say more – for example: 'I can see you're wanting to sit really close with me today, I wonder if it's difficult to do this with your mum, while she's holding your baby brother/sister?' Or the therapist senses whether to 'be' with the not-knowing, recognising that feeling confused, unsure, clumsy or frustrated, may be 'unconscious communications' that can be worked through with the client. Stern (1998) suggests that 'interpersonal communion, as created by attunement, will play an important role in the infant's coming to recognize that internal feeling states are forms of human experience that are shareable with other humans' (151).

Aspects of Booker's (2011) 'elemental play' encourage reciprocal interactions in these sessions, such as turn-taking through vocal and movement mirroring or joint reference books or toys. These tools of arts therapy can encourage a shared awareness, 'with each one's contributions being influenced by the contribution of the other' (p.82). When themes of resistance or avoidance are present through the client's body language, facial gestures and/or vocalisations, this can be noted with the client: 'I see you want the doll put away today'. If individuals are not interested in engaging with the 'creative invitations' offered by the therapist, this is respected, being mindful of not alienating the child by having an enforced plan for the session.

Throughout these sessions, and after they have ended, any favourite toys, pages from books, pictures or activities are communicated by the therapist to the teacher and family, who simultaneously have been using the same books with the child in class or at home. This encourages continuity and comprehension for the child and helps to ensure they know that others are continuing to hold their experience in mind, beyond their therapy sessions. Adam's mother, Jenny commented:

> The social story was invaluable in helping Adam. It not only helped him process the change visually, but it was also something we could work on together as a family.

A teacher (2020), who used a 'new baby' sibling story book in class stated:

> He loves books in general. However, he preferred to look at his 'new baby sibling' book than any other. He became very excited, when seeing me bring out his book and pointed at the photographs, particularly those with his whole family together. It was clear the book was important to him.

A Shared Place to Play

As the new sibling becomes a toddler, the family is invited to be part of a 'Siblings Family Group', the aim of which is to support the developing 'sibling dynamic'. Weekly sessions involve a parent or carer from each family, their child with a learning disability and the younger sibling. These groups are facilitated by the dramatherapist and a music therapist. In order to hold and contain the complexity that can arise when working within a multi-family model, the therapists 'parent' the group, as they provide a balance between structure and free play (Bull 2008). After a thirty-minute session, the older siblings return to their class. The adults use the remaining thirty minutes to reflect together on their experience of the session, while the younger siblings are supported to play together.

In between sessions, through joint reflection and peer supervision, the therapists are able to note any common themes, as well as their own emotional response to the group process. These reflections inform activities for following sessions. In this way, the structure of the group itself continues to evolve and grow with the participants. Prior to the start of the group, the therapists establish a relationship with each family (Jacobsen & Thompson 2017) by carrying out a home visit; information about the family is shared and any questions answered. Ellinor (2019, 7) writes about the importance of creating such links in order to 'ensure that we [the therapists] have a clear understanding of the family history' to contextualise the child.

Case Study – Family Triad

When Adam's little sister, Sienna, turned two, he, Sienna and their mum, Jenny, joined the Sibling Family Group with two other families. The therapy sessions began and ended with the group sitting on chairs in a circle singing the same 'hello' and 'goodbye' song. In between these structured 'bookends', turn-taking activities such as 'pass the feather' were introduced. Activities such as these, that combined coordination, sensory play, movement and song, had an important function in the early weeks, gently encouraging focus and connections to be made between all group members. In the talking time following the creative arts session, parents also tentatively started to connect as they shared their child's journeys to diagnosis and starting school.

Emerging Self-Expressions

Over time, the repetition of various activities became embedded within the session structure. This predictability encouraged familiarity for the children, who could then spontaneously make the activities their own. This was evident in the reciprocity of the sibling relationship between Adam and Sienna. On one occasion when Sienna was tickling Adam with the feather, he held the end of it and then allowed her to move it back and forth through his fingers. This was a moment of initiative and connection between them both.

Adam's responses to the wider group were initially hesitant, but became more confident and purposeful over time. In the 'How are you feeling today?' song, Adam began to make quiet but considered scratching and tapping sounds on the drum. By allowing time for Adam to respond, and by verbally reflecting on his playing, the therapists demonstrated to Adam that the group had noted and valued his contribution. Sienna also began to find her place and took great pleasure in directing the group, often choosing what activity should come next.

Cross-Family Relationships within the Group

Adam demonstrated a close relationship with his mum from the outset, often leaning his body towards her for reassurance. Over the weeks, he started to initiate contact with the therapists in a similar manner and began to share activities more readily with the other group members. Sienna too grew in confidence and became increasingly keen to interact with other siblings in the group. Loth (2008) writes of the unique dimension offered by the multi-family model, in that it potentially offers the members a sense of hope as 'they see other families learn, change and grow, as they receive support and encouragement from other families' (p. 60).

Just as important as the encouragement to share and take turns, was the opportunity for the children to challenge one another in the therapeutic space. On one such occasion, Sienna snatched a toy back from a sibling from another family, after they had taken it from Adam. Whilst mum's first impulse was to tell Sienna off for this interaction, further reflection in the talking-time allowed mum to realise how protective Sienna was towards her brother, noting that she often referred to her sibling as 'my Adam'. The structure of the Sibling Family Group is such that it allows a safe, contained place for behaviours and rivalries to 'play out', but also a space to reflect on the unique underlying issues that may prompt those behaviours.

Keeping It in the Family

Due to changes in family circumstance, the membership of the therapy group gradually reduced until only Adam's family remained. The following weeks provided a regular opportunity for them to communicate in a playful and contained environment. Adam's older brother, Jake, unexpectedly joined for one session, when he had an inset day at his school. The three siblings showed a connection and familiarity when playing together, and this one-off experience provided another layer of integration and grounding for the family.

As the therapy moved towards the planned ending, the sibling communication during the session developed further; Adam began to anticipate some of the activities, on one occasion kissing the top of Sienna's head when she approached him to say hello. During one of the final sessions, Adam placed both his arms out on the Gathering Drum in order to share the feather with his sister. Following this, all three family members overlapped their arms together on the drum. This was a 'golden moment' of connection between them all and demonstrated how far Adam's communication and shared connection skills had progressed over the years.

Beyond the therapy room, Adam's communication in class had improved greatly, and at home, Jenny reported that the siblings were playing together more. In the wider family context, Jenny talked of Adam's growing independence at family events. In her feedback after the sessions had finished, Jenny wrote:

> As each session progressed, both Adam and Sienna's confidence has grown immensely […] It has helped me to interact in a way I would never have, had it not been for the sessions.

Adam and his families' experience of the sibling family group illustrate that by enabling different strands of family dynamics to be explored together as a family in a group setting, the child with a learning disability can also be supported to integrate and internalise his or her experience of 'groups', both inside and outside the family.

Time to Be 'Me'

> My brother is different. I know this is true. Because of him, my life is different too.
> (Morvay 2010, 48)

The feeling of having a different life to one's peers, as described by Morvay, is one that throws up a unique set of challenges to the half a million young siblings in the UK with a brother or sister who has a learning disability (Sibs 2020). Parent's attention can be dominated by their disabled child; therefore, whether older or younger, their siblings often become independent with their own self-care from an early age, as well as sometimes taking on roles as 'young carers', helping with hoisting, feeding or keeping their sibling safe. As they reach developmental milestones that their brother or sister may never achieve, they become acutely aware of the different family roles they experience in comparison to their peers at school. Sibs (2020) highlight the importance of speaking to siblings about disability or illness, noting that it 'improves understanding, helps sibling relationships, maintains trust'.

Without an outlet to discuss or explore the complex feelings that having a sibling with a learning disability evokes, mental health may be impacted. On their national support website for children and families, The Anna Freud Centre (2020) notes 'We know more about children's mental health than we have ever done before. Yet mental health disorders continue to rise […] only a small proportion of children and young people who need support are getting it' (Anna Freud National Centre for Children and Families).

Growing the Service: Siblings Days

In 2011, a dramatherapy pilot project ran to support two siblings from the same family. They were referred for ten weekly forty-five-minute sessions after school. The intervention aimed to explore themes and feelings related to family life and encourage an opportunity to play and be nurtured. Although successful, the scheme was logistically unsustainable, as one had to travel across the borough to their sibling's school after their own school day. It was therefore proposed to organise a holiday activity group for siblings.

Since the initial pilot, the Siblings Days have grown and become well established. They initially catered for siblings aged 4–11 years, but as interest grew, an older group was established for teenage siblings aged 12–18 years. These workshops provide a dedicated time for siblings to reflect on their home-life with peers who have shared similar experiences. Service user evaluation forms reveal siblings enjoy meeting other siblings, acting out stories, making music and free-time playing together. Participants consistently state they are keen to attend again.

As well as creating much-needed connections, attendees are centre stage, with *their* needs and care being encouraged and attended to first and foremost. Barnet Young Carers (2019) cite, 'For some young carers, getting out and about with friends isn't always an option due to other priorities'. Therefore, the focus of these days is primarily one of enjoyment: playing, being supported and being creative, individually and as a group.

Therapeutic Holding

The workshops are specifically devised and facilitated by a member of the arts therapy team, encouraging siblings to feel nurtured while sharing feelings together. Due to their infrequency, these sessions are not 'therapy' but aim to be therapeutic. For some, attending the siblings group may be the only place they feel able to speak openly and frankly about their experience of having a sibling with a learning disability. The benefit of this intervention taking place within their sibling's environment means group facilitators have a specific understanding of their siblings learning needs. With this knowledge, they can encourage direct links between those who may have a brother or sister with similar issues like challenging behaviour, high medical care needs, frequent trips to hospital, and communication difficulties. Requests have also been made for cousins to join the group, particularly when they too are in a shared household and/or taking an active part with care and support.

'About Learning Disabilities', a website aimed at supporting parents, notes, 'Siblings of children with learning disabilities often worry about bringing school friends home to play' (About Learning Disabilities 2019). However, at the siblings workshop, the children and young people find a shared community that helps individuals gain a greater understanding of their own identity within their caring role. Even if the children do not ask directly or talk together about their similar circumstances, they clearly gravitate towards each other. When noticing this, as a team, the facilitators can help the children to ask their parents to arrange playdates with friends they have made in the group.

Primary Age Siblings Group

Despite not being labelled as therapy, therapeutic structures are introduced to help the sessions feel safe and contained. An art-based working agreement is established with all members and written on a large scroll of paper at the beginning of the day. It includes creating a non-judgmental space where 'all feelings are welcome'. This is put on the wall and referred to throughout the day. Ritualised activities provide structure and familiarity, while suggestions offered by participants are incorporated into the day. This enables the children and young people to feel they are being seen and heard, giving agency to their choices, which in turn inform ideas and rationales for future sessions. Information is shared and handed over between the therapists, if they have not been running the day together.

A session structure based on the Sesame Approach of dramatherapy (The Royal Central School of Speech and Drama 2021) is extended across the whole day (Figure 2.1).

Focus	Create a shared working alliance Name games
Warm up	Imaginative and feeling based warm up activities to encourage group connection (eg. 'Anyone who' game where siblings ask one another questions; 'anyone whose brother or sister is non-verbal?').
Bridge In	Games and activities introducing ideas linked to the main 'storytelling' event. Themes include; unlikely hero, competition, friendship, resilience, choice, the heroes journey, team work, special skills, feelings and 'being seen'. A story is told; eg. Grandmother Spider / Grimm tales eg. The Four Clever Brothers or The Queen Bee. The stories include themes of endurance, companionship, sibling rivalry, working together and overcoming obstacles, (often through humility and integrity).
Lunch break - Free play; opportunities to use the playground equipment / soft play	
Bridge In Main Event	'Check in' to remind all / add to the working alliance. Time to refocus following 'free play' at lunch time. Participants are encouraged to recap the story and reflect on the themes present. Individuals choose roles / characters they would like to play for a spontaneous enactment and create props and costumes. At the group's discretion adults in the school are invited to watch the enactment. (Siblings and staff are interested to meet one another. Children enjoy the staff guessing who their sibling is. This playful celebration again encourages community and a sense of normalcy, which is too often absent from their lives.)
Bridge Out	De-role games and reflection activities encouraging opportunities to be seen, appreciated and feel connected (eg. 'I want to swap chairs with X because during the day I appreciated when they...')
Grounding	Individuals choose how the group say 'Goodbye' to them Participants fill out an evaluation form with reflections from the day (generating input and ideas for future sessions).

Figure 2.1 Dramatherapy structure in the Sesame Approach.

Supporting a Safe Space

Where possible, sibling sessions are run in parallel with the special school's holiday play-scheme. This provides additional respite for parents, who are able to drop their children off together. Jenny (2020) fed back:

> The sibling workshops gave Jake the opportunity to come into Adam's school and meet staff that work with Adam. It gave him the opportunity to meet other siblings and share his feelings and emotions.

A Learning Support Assistant from the school staff also supports the day, taking part in activities and modelling participation. This has been particularly useful when some siblings themselves have additional learning needs. All adults facilitating carefully manage group dynamics to ensure other sibling participants do not take on a 'carer' role during the day. From when the first Siblings Days were set up, members of staff who identified themselves as sibling carers stepped forward to assist. They have added an additional rich element to the planning with suggested ideas and their deep empathic engagement, which often emerged during the sessions. When appropriate, they shared with the group moments and experiences from their own sibling relationships. The children and young people are often curious to hear from, and respond to, an adult who really understands 'life in their shoes'.

Teenage Siblings Group

The first teenage sibling group to be run included Adam's brother, Jake, who had made friends with peers around the same age in the 'younger' sessions. Appreciating that older siblings often want to be more independent in the holidays, 'Teens Sibs' were established as a half day, three-hour session. Using a similar, condensed structure from the 'Young Siblings Day', the teenage provision was adapted to provide more talking space, to share and listen to one another's direct experiences. Similar to the parents' talking time in the Family Siblings Therapy Group, teenage siblings often talk candidly about painful emotional experiences related to their siblings. Themes include fears for the future, life expectancy of their siblings and responsibilities into adulthood. They share difficulties around their siblings' challenging behaviours, where they may 'hurt themselves or others. They might hit, kick, bite, scratch or scream. Siblings tell us…[this] can make them feel unsafe, sad or frightened' (Young Sibs 2018). As well as this, they appreciate sharing golden moments of connection with their brother or sister, which may not be understood by peers within their own social groups. Milestones, such as their sibling becoming toilet trained, means they no longer need to support them with as much intimate care. 'It is important to remember that whilst there are difficulties to be faced as a member of a "Specially Blended Family" […] there are many positive aspects to living as part of a diverse family unit too' (About Learning Disabilities 2019). The older siblings listen intensely to one another's experiences. They find collective similarities and understanding from peers who can relate to their experiences, such as their personal belongings repeatedly being damaged. They acutely understand one another's difficulties like finding a private space for homework or spending time with a friend. This in turn supports personal affirmation of the uniquely different situation in which they find themselves.

Feedback from the service users has provided effective quantitative research data for the school, directly evidencing the benefits of the provision, which can be shared with the Parent Staff Association (PSA) who fund the work, governors and Ofsted. To further promote the sessions, some reflections from the sibling's evaluation forms are shared, with consent, on the school blog, along with one or two photographs from the day. This increases visibility and another chance for participants to be seen and heard, demonstrating how they are valued as part of our wider school community.

Jake (2020) reflecting on his time attending activity days:

> Sibling groups were great, I got to meet the staff at Adam's school and they got to know me. I got to see Adam's classroom, his pictures and his work displayed on the walls. I like that I got to meet other siblings just like me! ...... I will always have good memories of my time there.

Conclusion

> Be nice to your siblings; they are your best link to your past and the people most likely to stick with you in the future.
> (Baz Lurhmann – Everybody's Free to Wear Sunscreen 1999)

The benefits of providing therapeutic sessions addressing sibling dynamics within the context of children with learning disabilities have enriched the school's practices and relationships within families. A variety of interventions have been explored and developed in order to offer ways to support a child and their family to develop understanding around change, emotional development, attachment, resilience, independence, sharing, self and other. The vignettes in this chapter have highlighted the benefits of systemic work, where all aspects of the child's world are supported within their school. They demonstrate how therapeutic interventions with various family members can be further explored at home, by encouraging 'affect attunement' to change 'the other by providing something the other did not have before or, if it was present, by consolidating it' (Stern 1998, 144). This enables family members to feel empowered to normalise and discuss their feelings more openly at home, thus continuing the theme of integration for all.

The aims, process and evaluation shared throughout this chapter have highlighted strengths and challenges from these areas of work – including golden moments – and service user feedback. It is hoped that, in doing so, this will provide useful information and ideas for facilitators who would like to integrate or develop systemic family work within their practice, working therapeutically with children with learning disabilities and their sibling dynamics.

References

About Learning Disabilities. (2019) *Support for Siblings of Young People With Learning Disabilities.* http://www.aboutlearningdisabilities.co.uk/support-for-siblings-young-people-with-learning-disabilities.html (Accessed 30 May 2020).

Anna Freud National Centre for Children and Families. https://www.annafreud.org/about-us/what-we-do/ (Accessed 31 May 2020).

Barnet Young Carers. (2019) *Having Some Fun* http://barnetyoungcarers.org.uk (Accessed 31 May 2020).

Booker, M. (2011) *Developmental Drama; Dramatherapy Approaches for People with Profound or Severe Multiple Disabilities, Including Sensory Impairment.* London and Philadelphia, PA: Jessica Kingsley Publishers.

Bull, R. (2008) 'Autism and the Family: Group Music Therapy with Mothers and Children'. In: Oldfield, A. & Flower, C. (Eds.), *Music Therapy with Children and Their Families*, 71–87. London and Philadelphia, PA: Jessica Kingsley Publishers.

Civardi, A. (2005) *The New Baby – Usborne First Experiences.* London: Usborne Publishing Ltd.

Crimmens, P. (2006) *Drama Therapy and Storymaking in Special Education.* London and Philadelphia, PA: Jessica Kingsley Publishers.

Ellinor, J. (2019) 'It's the 'group' That Matters: Dramatherapy Working with a Group of Parents and Their Children Who Have Profound and Multiple Learning Difficulties.' In: *Dramatherapy Journal.* Volume 40, Issue 1. London: SAGE Journals.

French, L. & Klein, R. eds. (2012) *Therapeutic Practice in Schools; Working with the Child Within: A Clinical Workbook for Counsellors, Psychotherapists and Arts Therapists.* London and New York: Routledge.

Gerhardt, S. (2004) *Why Love Matters.* London: Routledge.

Gray, C. & Garand, J. (1993) 'Social Stories: Improving Responses of Individuals with Autism with Accurate Social Information'. In: *Focus on Autistic Behavior. Journal of Autism and other Developmental Disabilities.* Volume 8, Issue 1, 1–10. London: Sage Journals.

Hewett, D., Firth, G., Barber, M. & Harrison, T. (2011) *The Intensive Interaction Handbook.* London: Sage.

Jacobsen, S. L. & Thompson, G. (2017) 'Working with Families. Emerging Characteristics'. In: Jacobsen, S. L. & Thompson, G. (Eds.), *Music Therapy with Families: Therapeutic Approaches and Theoretical Perspectives*, 309–326. London: Jessica Kingsley Publishers.

Loth, H. (2008) 'Music Therapy Groups for Families with a Learning-disabled Toddler: Bridging Some Gaps.' In: Oldfield, A. & Flower, C. (Eds.), *Music Therapy with Children and their Families*, 53–69. London and Philadelphia, PA: Jessica Kingsley Publishers.

Lurhmann, B. (1999) *Everybody's Free to Wear Sunscreen* https://www.youtube.com/watch?v=5giWfpANMac (Accessed 27 June 2020).

Morvay, B. (2010) *My Brother Is Different – A Sibling's Guide to Coping with Autism.* Washington, DC: Library of Congress.

National Autistic Society – https://www.autism.org.uk/about/strategies/social-stories-comic-strips.aspx (Accessed 10 June 2020).

Picture Exchange Communication System. (PECS) (2020). https://pecs-unitedkingdom.com/pecs/ (Accessed 28 June 2020).

Sibs. https://www.sibs.org.uk (Accessed 26 May 2020).

Stern, D. (1998) T*he Interpersonal World of the Infant*. London: Karnac.

The Royal Central School of Speech and Drama (2021) *Drama and Movement Therapy MA* https://www.cssd.ac.uk/courses/drama-and-movement-therapy-ma (Accessed 30 March 2021).

Young Sibs. (2018) *For Brothers or Sisters of Disabled Children and Adults – Challenging Behaviour* https://www.youngsibs.org.uk/info-and-advice/difficult-behaviour/challenging-behaviour/ (Accessed 30 March 2021).

Chapter 3

'May we speak for you?'

Thoughts on a Multi-Vocal Approach When Working with Clients with Profound and Multiple Learning Difficulties (PMLD) within an Education Setting

Luke Simonds

As a dramatherapist working in a special education setting for children with severe learning difficulties (SLD), I do not work alone. When it comes to working with any child, there is the potential for many voices to be advocating for them. There are parents, carers, extended family members, teachers, teaching assistants, occupational therapists, arts therapists, speech and language therapists, doctors, nurses, educational psychologists, social workers, physiotherapists, social care teams, local authority representatives and respite care workers. All these individuals comprise the team around a child.

This collective is powerful: educated, informed, concerned and focused. Each member, although possibly loathe to admit it, has a slightly different agenda, albeit one still centred on the child.

An additional complexity in writing this chapter is that as well as being a dramatherapist, I hold the role of assistant head teacher within the special education setting, in which I practise. Even within myself, there is more than one voice crying out for what is needed for any specific child.

The role of the Chorus in the classical Greek drama is a useful theatrical metaphor here. In theatre, the Chorus is considered a 'fragmented group with diverse views' (Wiles 2000, 125), providing a commentary on the action, with the many voices contained within it, though occasionally speaking as one. Although they sometimes serve to underline what is the principal focus of the performance, they can also undermine, argue and distract.

To follow this metaphor, we, as the team around the child, are that chorus. The actor in our performance is the child with profound and multiple learning difficulties (PMLD). Does this chorus drown out the 'voice' of our principal character? Will the team's intention or beliefs distract or detract from what the child is telling us? Lecoq (1997, 139–140) says of the Chorus that it has the ability to both oppose and unite.

How do we know if our child's truth is heard among all of these voices, when the child's voice is potentially inaudible, or due to the complexity of need for that child, it is very difficult to understand what they are trying to convey?

DOI: 10.4324/9781003091783-5

Finding the truth of the child in this interlinking personal and professional narrative is a potential quagmire. The offers, comments, suggestions and assumptions that are made from this team around the client can aid the therapist's attempt to engage with the authentic voice of that child. But it can impede it too. The power of the combined voice can seem almost 'superhuman' (Wiles 2000, 132) in its ability to distract the therapist from listening to the client's own truth.

It is the harmony of this collective voice which concerns us here. How do we ensure harmony of group voice and then quieten that voice so that we can really listen to the child? Is it even possible? Is the goal to have these dissonant voices be present, alongside one another, in a way that can be allowed?

Developing interpretations of children's meanings is certainly an important (and contested) topic. I wonder if there is untapped potential for developing new ways of thinking about children with PMLD when working with them by using dramatherapy and new ways of supporting therapeutic interaction using a team. The literature written by specialist PMLD practitioners is well known. Without going into detail here, I will mention four books that have had significant impact on both my teaching and dramatherapy practice: *Educating Children with Profound and Multiple Learning Difficulties* (Ware 1994), *The PMLD Ambiguity* (Simmons & Watson 2014), *Engaging Learners with Complex Learning Difficulties and Disabilities* (Carpenter et al 2015) and *Developmental Drama* (Booker 2011). I identify with these authors in their approach to working with a child with PMLD, whose view of the world can be summed up by Simmons and Watson (2014, 89): that the child encounters the world in a raw, sensuous, abstract state, unfiltered by context or history.

I wonder if, rather than taking the child's view as my start point, I could take the perspective of the whole team around the child, using the lens of Greek classical drama. I would like to re-visit the Greek theatre form in order to take my practice in a new direction. It is my hope that this might lead to an original contribution that extends our consideration of the solo dramatherapist working in the field of PMLD. I have used a children's fictional story that borrows from the idea of a Greek Chorus.

Click, Clack, Moo, Cows That Type

In framing this chapter around the children's story, titled *Click, Clack, Moo, Cows That Type* (Cronin & Lewin 2002), I aim to explore my therapeutic work through the story's narrative, which I believe in turn reflects the function of the Greek Chorus. The story acts as a metaphor for my role as therapist in an education setting (the farmer), the education professionals I work with (the cows) and the children (the other animals on the farm, e.g. the ducks).

In the story, the cows are empowered through their ability to use a typewriter, which gives them voice and an ability to communicate effectively (they think) with the farmer. As a result, the cows advocate for all the other animals on the farm. They infer what they know from their relationships with the animals in order to make requests of the farmer. For instance, they believe the ducks are cold and need blankets. Do these requests meet the animals' needs and are the animals truly being heard? The farmer thinks he knows what all the animals need. The cows' own needs have an impact on what they believe is right. Inevitably, it transpires that the animals do not understand the cows' inaccurate requests and they are forced to find other ways to make their needs known. The ducks do not need blankets; what they want is a diving board for their duck-pond.

I have used this story to drive both drama teaching and dramatherapy sessions within a school setting. Farm animals are a rich source of auditory and performative stimulation for children, both in their attempts to communicate and by their movement. The key theme is miscommunication and misunderstanding cloaked by good intention. The story can be enhanced by group performance. Children can come together to take on the roles of the cows or the ducks. The children are then working together in their recitation of the narrative. Staff can also take on a role as one of the animal chorus and model expectations for the children. The story themes of listening to and supporting one another apply to both children and colleagues, which is why I was initially drawn to it. I chose the book to read to a class as the animal noises (voices) could be used to dramatic and humorous effect. The message of the tale serves to educate the child and the adult. The animal collectives within the story reflect the animal Chorus' evident in Greek theatre, serving to embody a 'collective wisdom' (Wiles 2000, 142). For me, this echoes the collective wisdom that a dramatherapist may encounter when working with a child. Sometimes, it can be very hard to challenge or to extend an established collective view.

Typically, when working with children with PMLD, you are not alone in the room with them. Teaching staff and/or teaching assistants may be present in the space, as additional support. Often what tends to happen in these sessions is that the therapist finds staff members commenting on the action of the child or becoming more involved in supporting the child than the therapist would prefer. It is essential that, before work begins, the therapist and the teaching staff discuss how much support should be given to a child during the session, and an agreement or contract drawn up, so that the child can be free to respond to the unfolding theatrical narrative in whatever way they choose. This is easier said than done in some cases, as supporting adults often feel that their prior experience and relationship with the child should inform the work of the therapist and thereby the experience within the session. Just like the bovine characters in the story, who think they are helping the ducks, staff advocate for the other (the child). The dramatherapist is much like the farmer in the story – who in turn is much like the farmer in Aristophanes' 'The Acharnians' (Wiles 2000, 28) – in trying to hear the needs of these disparate voices. Advocating for the other is borne of care and goodwill, but they can distract and obscure. My choice of the story of cows and ducks is an attempt to remind us all that sometimes our involvement as advocates for the child is inhibiting their ability to 'speak' for themselves and to ultimately be truly 'heard'.

Akin to Bateson's 'Metalogue' (1972, 12), the rules of therapeutic conversation need to be considered. In order to hear, we cannot exist in isolation from the rest of those many voices wanting to advocate and speak for the client. So, what constitutes therapeutic intervention with an individual with PMLD? How do we contain the safe space, when it might be filled with a great many individuals alongside the client? It demands of the dramatherapist a need to reframe what the client conversation might sound like – and indeed the therapy room might look like.

It is vital that the therapist *in situ* capitalises on the systems that are in place within the educational setting, in order to ensure that there is a commonality in understanding between what therapists intend and what the educational setting wants for the child. By aligning themselves with the educational organisation, the therapist can be more effective when working with the child. The therapeutic alliance has to first begin with the setting, before the child can be truly met. A shared language is needed.

It is important that the therapist draws on the knowledge of the practitioners within the team. The therapist will hopefully find there is a plethora of useful resources for therapy work that are being used by educational practitioners, such as the social emotional communication approaches expounded by Hewett and Firth's *Intensive Interaction* (2012), the Social Communication, Emotional Regulation and Transactional Support (SCERTS) model (Prizant et al 2014) and Low Arousal Supports Educational Resilience (LASER) (Morewood 2020). They all refer to the benefits of working with a child of achieving 'joint attention' (Prizant et al 2014, 3), in trying to build a 'shared understanding' (Hewett & Firth 2012, 2, 5) which will support communication and emotional regulation.

Hewett and Firth's Intensive Interaction model chimes with the therapeutic approach, in that it is a non-intrusive technique employed to build a relationship, and ultimately communication, with a client. At its essence, it is a process of 'echoing' (Caldwell 2006, 13); using our client's own non-verbal body language as a means to communicate. We mirror what we see from them. As therapists, we are familiar with the idea of recognising and reflecting our client's body language. The Intensive Interaction model is commonly employed within special educational settings. It can go some way to allaying our staff team's fear that if they aren't heard advocating for the child, they aren't working hard enough. Intensive Interaction is, simply put, a way of mirroring and reflecting back what an adult sees from a child. In the way the Greek Chorus can act as an alternative reflection on the action on stage, it gives an opportunity for another perspective to be seen. The danger can sometimes be that, just like our Greek Chorus, on occasion, the adults' perspective can stray too far from the truth of the child we are focused on.

For many of our neurotypical colleagues in special education settings, Maitland's (2008) observation that 'silence is a place of non-being' (117) is still an instinctive default position. For the child with PMLD, silence should be seen as an opportunity. As support staff, we often still feel obliged to fill that silence. Maitland (2014) also points out that for many of us, we have grown up without silence and solitude, because we have been educated through a model that puts a strong focus on engagement and stimulation. I still find myself speaking for the client during a therapeutic intervention when it is not necessary. Why can't we be engaged through silence and solitude? Models such as Intensive Interaction aim to silence us, in order that we can hear more accurately. As a relatively low-cost/high-impact model, it 'gets the best out of our staff, and this in turn will allow us to see the best in the people we support' (Mouriere & McKim 2018, 18).

'May we listen to you?'

I wonder at this point whether this chapter should be called, 'May we listen to you?'

In listening, we are seeking 'Co-production not collaboration' (Morewood 2020) with our clients. Even before we work with a person, we have already assumed certain things about that person, rather than developing an approach, together, in the moment. Why not reframe our agenda in favour of silence? Can silence be an agenda? Maitland states that as therapists, 'we create and hold the free silence' (2008, 248), in order that from the silence, the client may seek their truth.

It was in some ways uncomfortable for me, when working in a special education setting, to realise that many of my colleagues were more experienced than I was in using and embedding a therapeutic model (Intensive Interaction) into a child's everyday learning curriculum. And yet, I was THE qualified therapist. If I did not learn from the institution's skillset, I would be foolish. To set myself apart from the everyday workings of the setting would be to disable myself and my relationship with my clients. The therapist's view of a sanctified therapy room where a one-to-one intervention occurs is challenged by this. The dramatherapist must be less like Cronin's reactive farmer and more like Aristophanes' farmer who is a 'breaker of ritual rules' (Wiles 2000, 29).

Breaking the Rules

I was working with a young adult, whom I shall call Jackson. Jackson is a wheelchair user with PMLD. He has limited use of his legs but has considerably developed upper body strength. When out of his wheelchair and on the ground, he is very ambulant and can crawl at speed. He has no formalised spoken word communication and only limited signing skill. He responds to adult voices, particularly deep vocal tones. He relishes the energy and sound of a group environment. He cannot read in the traditional sense but relishes the physical characteristics of books. He is stimulated by hard back picture books and will 'read' them by flicking the pages with his fingers at rapid speed.

Sustaining social interaction with Jackson can be challenging. On this occasion, Jackson had taken his usual residence by his bookshelf in the classroom, sitting on the floor, reading his favourite books. This was a quieter classroom moment, where Jackson and I were alone, and I saw an opportunity for the two of us to share some time together. Employing intensive interaction techniques, I sat with him and picked up a book, mirroring his posture and activity. Jackson, after a short while, seemed to become aware of me. He threw down his book on to the laminate floor in front of him with an entertaining thump. I repeated the action, shortly after, with my own book. Jackson smiled and crawled towards me, picking up my book. I picked up another book and shortly after threw it down on the floor again, sliding back on the floor, mirroring Jackson's movements. Jackson moved to follow and picked up the book with a smile. This was repeated numerous times. Classroom staff, although engaged in the task supporting other children, witnessed this interaction. A simple narrative unfolded where between us we created a crawling, sliding, twisting, turning path of discarded books, which he and I travelled along, together.

Is It Therapy?

The intervention above lasted no more than ten minutes but was a sustained relational interaction. I had capitalised on the moment and engaged in what I considered a therapeutic intervention with Jackson. Jackson had accepted my offer to create this simple dramatic narrative – 'the pathway of books' – which in itself led to a sustained shared experience. Had Jackson and I been in the therapy space, Jackson may not have felt comfortable enough to engage in that way. Within the busy classroom space, I was able to be fully present for him, showing 'an openness and anticipation for the unknown' (McCarthy 2008, 47), that became an invitation for Jackson to be authentic. The movement and play modalities employed here are devices I would use in the therapy space. However, I was in the classroom space. I was a teacher sidestepping into my therapist role. If I am to become the therapist in that moment, I need to ensure it is safe to do so. I need to make sure that the place where this therapeutic intervention happens is respected by the other staff and young people who are close by. This requires that a prior discussion is held with the supporting staff to establish the conditions within which this kind of drama can spontaneously occur, and that ground rules are set in place to ensure it is safe for it to do so.

It feels important, at this juncture, to discuss briefly how one might practically assess or evaluate this kind of intervention. Education practitioners and therapists are expected to formally assess the impact of a learning or therapeutic intervention, often using very different ways. For children with PMLD, assessment can be a problematic process, as development, response or change over time can be very gradual. A tool that I have found useful in this regard is *Routes for Learning* (RfL) (Llywoddraeth Cymru 2020). RfL is an education assessment tool for early cognitive development, communication and social interaction, as well as an individual's interaction with the environment. Although principally an educational resource, I have found it helpful in applying to therapeutic interventions. In the school setting that I am in, it is helpful to explain the aims and outcomes of the dramatherapy sessions in language familiar to education practitioners. Tools such as RfL help to do this when working with children with PMLD, as well as other forms of learning difficulty. It is important for the dramatherapist to align their approach as closely as possible with that of the setting. It is my experience that this can go some way to seeding, and then embedding, the dramatherapist's intentions for their own sessions within the school day. This alignment of the educator and the dramatherapist's approach in order to provide the optimum level of support for these young people is my ultimate intention.

My story is an example of the strength of the combined voice of teacher and therapist in what I deemed to be a sensitive approach to blurring the boundary between the learning and therapy space in that moment. In truth, this may not seem an unusual occurrence. Teaching practitioners may often enter into a similar interaction with a child with PMLD. Does my role as therapist allow me to have heightened awareness of the value of this relational opportunity? I believe it does. But the blurring between teaching and therapy space can be a concern for the therapist. As mentioned above, there are times when a therapist has to be the embodiment of a movable therapy space in the school setting and be able to catch any opportunity to create a safe space for the child to explore their experience. It is my view that the dramatherapist *is* the safe space. The dramatherapist has the capacity to build this special relationship with the child because of their awareness of the therapeutic role they inhabit and the many ways it can manifest. It is my view that the formal contained setting of the therapy room is but one mode available to the therapist in the school setting. The opportunity to be 'available' in other ways is also vitally important.

This 'availability' of the therapist sometimes can be expanded to include group therapy situations. Opportunities to include other children can present themselves. Another example featuring Jackson was a dance/movement lesson from the classroom space next door. Upon hearing the dance/pop music playing in the adjacent space, Jackson crawled to where his peers were dancing and joined in a physical and social opportunity, engaging in eye contact and a joyously shared physical experience. This expressive movement became 'conversation and contact of another kind' (Chesner 1995, 46), and because it was initiated by Jackson himself, it was important to capitalise on its occurrence.

It seems our Greek Chorus is thus expanding again to include the voices of other children. As in traditional group therapy interventions, they reflect and sometimes amplify the 'voice' of our child client. And as the chorus grows, I ask myself again, do we create a controlling environment when working with clients that cannot speak (in traditional terms)? There is a chorus of voices that infer what they *think* we hear and see from our child. Is this collaboration? This is a client that can, apparently, only communicate through physical responses to stimulus, or vocalisations, that are developmental antecedents to spoken language, as we know it. Like the cows in our story, we might decide what we think we hear and see and ascribe a perceived state to the client. Our position as therapist can be aided or distorted by the team around that child. When the notion of a safe therapeutic space is questioned in the school setting, we must be continually mindful of the potential for dilution of the special role the therapist holds. Our therapeutic approach can become just more voices in the Greek Chorus, potentially drowning out the client's voice. It is important that the child knows that the therapeutic relationship is still available. Subsequently, there is a burden on the therapist to be very mindful of how these interactions are framed.

Silence and Disarmament

I find myself returning to the need for silence! Silence in order to hear the child's true voice. The necessity for the traditional therapy-room space, where there is an opportunity for the client's 'self-emptying' and/or 'self-outpouring' (Maitland 2008, 251). It is important to note that this silence is not just for the client but for the therapist also, who in my special education setting (and probably others) is assailed by opinions relating to the client and who needs solace in order to focus. Is there a place in this flexible safe-space model for both kinds of therapeutic practice?

The flexible safe-space model I posit, where the therapist is capitalising on therapeutic opportunity as it occurs in the moment, puts significant pressure on the therapist. Using themselves as the supportive container means the dramatherapist has to rigorously ensure therapeutic integrity. It is what I call 'therapy as disarmament': where the child may not realise that they are in a therapeutic situation or relationship, and that they are exploring themselves through the work they are doing. Prior to training as a dramatherapist, as a teacher I often thought that lessons in Social, Emotional and Mental Health (SEMH) topics where I used dramatic devices, such as stories and role-play, was 'therapy by another name'. The lesson content would directly relate to the needs of the child involved. They would be exploring their own material without realising it. However, in a therapeutic relationship the child client and the therapist must have the opportunity to find a way to *reflect* on what has just occurred during the session.

Conclusion

As dramatherapists, we are comfortable with a certain level of ambiguity. The nature of our work includes finding our way through the complexities of the unspoken. We are able to infer meaning from what we hear the client say and what we see the client do. This ambiguity can only be compounded when those clients do not speak and have limited advocacy of their own bodies. Can we empower their agency, to have their own 'voice' and for that voice to be heard by expanding the therapeutic space to include the classroom?

In drawing this chapter to a conclusion, I refer again to Bateson's 'Metalogue' (1972, 12): this is a problematic conversation we need to have about the very nature of the intervention we are having with the client with PMLD. In order to hear, we cannot exist in isolation from the rest of those advocates – the many voices that speak – for the client. So, what constitutes therapeutic intervention with an individual from this client group? How do we contain the safe space, when it is filled with a great many individuals alongside the client? It demands of the dramatherapist a need to reframe the client conversation and to adapt.

> The point is that the purpose of these conversations is to discover the 'rules'. It's like life – a game whose purpose is to discover the rules, which rules are always changing and always undiscoverable.
>
> (Bateson 1972, 30)

As dramatherapists, we need to continue to cultivate our awareness of the challenging cultural interactions within a multidisciplinary team. As dramatherapists we need to continue to evolve our 'mercurial role' (Holloway & Seebohm 2011, 12).

We need to change the rules. The community around the child, which our Chorus embodies, challenges our perception of the lone dramatherapist in his/her 'solitary quest' (Wiles 2000, 28). He is no longer the 'star actor who is everything and the chorus is nothing' (Wiles 2000, 22), but he is the '*Coryphaeus*' (Wiles 2000, 134): the leader and teacher setting the time that the other members of the chorus follow. The dramatherapist, although in strong alliance with the multitude of supportive voices, must himself be the safe space.

References

Bateson, G. 1972. *Steps to an Ecology of Mind.* San Francisco, CA: Chandler Pub. Co.

Booker, M. 2011. *Developmental Drama: Dramatherapy Approaches for People with Profound or Severe Multiple Disabilities, Including Sensory Impairment.* London: Jessica Kingsley Publishers.

Caldwell, P. 2006. *Finding You Finding Me.* London: Jessica Kingsley Publishers.

Carpenter, B., Egerton, J., Cockbill, B., Bloom, T., Fotheringham, J., Rawson, H. & Thistlethwaite, J. 2015. *Engaging Learners with Complex Learning Difficulties and Disabilities: A Resource Book for Teachers and Teaching Assistants.* Abingdon: Routledge Publishers.

Chesner, A. 1995. *Dramatherapy for People with Learning Disabilities: A World of Difference.* 2004 edition. London: Jessica Kingsley Publishers.

Cronin, D. & Lewin, B. 2002. *Click, Clack, Moo Cows That Type.* London: Simon & Shuster.

Hewett, D. & Firth, G. 2012. *Intensive Interaction Institute: Curriculum Documents for Schools.* Puckeridge: The Intensive Interaction Institute.

Holloway, P. & Seebohm, H. 2011. 'When Worlds Elide: Culture, Dialogue and Identity in Multi-Professional Settings'. In: *Dramatherapy Journal.* Volume 33, Issue 1, 4–15. London: Routledge.

Lecoq, J. 1997. 'Le corps poétique – un enseignement de la création théâtrale'. *Actes Sud -Papier 10* (Aries: Anrat 1997).

Llywoddraeth Cymru/Welsh Government. 2020. *Routes for Learning.* Addysyg Cymru/ Education Wales [Online] Available at: https://hwb.gov.wales/curriculum-for-wales/routes-for-learning [Accessed: 8 October 2020].

Maitland, S. 2008. *A Book of Silence*, 2nd Edition. London: Granta Publications.

Maitland, S. 2014. *How to be Alone*, digital edition. London: MacMillan Publishers Limited.

McCarthy, D. 2008. *Speaking about the Unspeakable: Non-Verbal Methods and Experiences in Therapy with Children*. London: Jessica Kingsley Publishers.

Morewood, G. 2020. *LASER (Low Arousal Supports Educational Resilience): Using Low Arousal Approaches in Learning Environments*, Studio III (www.studio3.org) [Online]. Available at: http://www.gdmorewood.com/conferences/list/ [Accessed: 11 May 2020].

Mouriere, A. & McKim, J. 2018. *Integrating Intensive Interaction*. Abingdon: Routledge.

Prizant, B.M., Wetherby, A., Rubin, E., Laurent, A.C. & Rydell, P. 2014. *The SCERTS Model: A Comprehensive Educational Approach for children with Autism Spectrum Disorders*, 4th Edition. Baltimore, MD: Paul H. Brookes Publishing Co.

Simmons, B. & Watson, D. 2014. *'The PMLD Ambiguity': Articulating the Life Worlds of Children with Profound and Multiple Learning Disabilities*. London: Routledge Publishers.

Ware, J. 1994. *Educating Children with Profound and Multiple Learning Difficulties*. London: David Fulton Publishers.

Wiles, D. 2000. *Greek Theatre Performance: An Introduction*. 2013 digital edition. Cambridge: Cambridge University Press.

Chapter 4

How Can We Track and Aid Emotional Development in Children and Young People with Learning Disabilities?

Helen Milward

Introduction

In 2012, the Eden Academy Trust formed to create a family of special schools in North West London. This facilitated the creation of the Arts Therapy team, bringing together the dramatherapists, music therapists and dance movement psychotherapists already directly employed by the schools. As a team working across four schools, we questioned the possibility of measuring and tracking changes in the pupils we work with. Taking into account the context of special education needs and disabilities (SEND) schools and the variances across ages and abilities in moderate learning disabilities (MLD), severe learning disabilities (SLD) and profound and multiple learning disabilities (PMLD), we began to construct a tool to be able to track pupil development within arts therapy sessions.

The creation, development and subsequent piloting of the relational, emotional, sense of self (RESOS) framework led me to present this evaluation tool at the 2016 British Association of Dramatherapists (BADth) annual conference. During the conference, I also attended Dr. Rinat Feniger-Schaal's paper: *Can Children with Severe Learning Disabilities Have Fun? A research study of the therapeutic clowning in kindergartens with children with intellectual disabilities* (Feniger-Schaal et al 2018). In a more recent paper, she stated that 'the literature on the social-emotional world of young people, […] with ID, is scarce' (Geigera et al 2020).

This statement surprised me. Working alongside a highly specialised and dedicated multi-professional team, speech and language therapists (SALT), occupational therapists (OT), physiotherapists (PT), educational psychologists and education staff, I had made an assumption that work with learning disabilities was well documented.

The research undertaken when creating RESOS had brought to light gaps in evaluation tools but not identified specific gaps in literature. The language used to describe the cognitive and developmental abilities of this client group has broadened and changed in order to better capture the individual. However, when we address our pupil's abilities in a developmental context, we still refer to neurotypical,

DOI: 10.4324/9781003091783-6

age-specific, developmental trackers in documents, such as *Developmental Matters in the Early Year Foundation Stages* (Moylett & Stewart 2012) or *What to Expect, When?* (Action for Children 2015), which track typical range of developments in children and offer guidance for practitioners to support and aid growth. Where were the measurement tools designed for children with learning disabilities?

To address this issue, I proposed a research project which was presented to the academy's board of trustees. The project took into account the evidence accumulated through the piloting and continued use of the RESOS framework, which had previously been presented to the board as part of a series of outcome measures. The rationale behind this research focused on:

- What research and literature exists into emotional development of people with learning disabilities, both within arts therapies and through other professions?
- How can emotional development in people with learning difficulties be tracked?
- Can a clear developmental guide be established? This may be dependent on variables such as dual diagnosis, range of MLD, SLD and PMLD.
- Are there clear indicators and/or methods which can aid emotional development?

This chapter summarises the research journey, alongside the use of RESOS, which works hand in hand with social-emotional mental Health (SEMH) outcomes from a pupil's Education Health and Care Plan (EHPC): a statement of needs for a pupil in a SEND setting. This chapter includes the following stages: the initial proposal of the project, including consent and approval from trustees, a literature review, the collection of data using a qualitative research methodology and practical clinical interventions. It includes key findings and some illustrative case material. The intention is to make available the full research project and RESOS framework in future publications.

Setting Up the Project

The research project set out to better understand and explore the possibility of being able to track a common emotional development in children and young people with learning disabilities.

The proposal followed the premise that neurotypical emotional development is well documented (Moylett & Stewart 2012; Action for Children 2015). It highlighted the benefits of understanding the emotional development of those with learning difficulties and provided greater insight into how we might meet the needs of our pupils.

A presentation for and discussion with the trustees ensured consent and ethical issues were identified and addressed. Full approval and funding, to cover additional hours required, was given by the board to carry out the research. Stages of the project delivery were set as follows:

1 Literature review of published works on the emotional development and therapeutic interventions with clients with learning difficulties.
2 Identification of specific gaps in the understanding of how those with learning
   difficulties develop emotionally, followed by an investigation to identify potential commonalities in developmental stages and how progress is tracked.
3 Direct dramatherapy interventions with a cross section of pupils across the
   academy schools with a variety of ages and abilities. Data was captured through
   questionnaires collating the perceptions of teachers and families, with a view to
   identifying any potential patterns of development.
4 Capturing the qualitative data and use of RESOS framework to annotate the
   possibility of tracking SEMH development and concluding how a multi-
   professional input can aid an individual's development, identifying appropriate
   and realistic milestones.

This project was carried out over two years, including 20 dramatherapy sessions
per each of the ten pupil participants.

Using the questions posed in the rationale, the above stages formed the structure
of the research design and framed the research journey.

Stage 1: What Research Exists?

The literature review began with a survey sent to the membership of the BADth,
British Association of Music Therapists (BAMT), Association of Dance Movement
Psychotherapists (ADMP) and British Association of Art Therapies (BAAT). The
review included an in-depth search through psychology-based online resources and
journals and learning disability-specific publications.

Significant literature on dramatherapy and learning disabilities repeatedly referenced Anna Chesner (1994, 1998), Jenny Pearson (1996), Marion Lindkvist
(1998), Paula Crimmins (2006), Mary Booker (2011) and Deborah Haythorne and
Anna Seymour eds. (2017). Notable publications from other arts therapists include
Tessa Watson (2007), Vicky Karkou (2010) and Helen Payne (2017). A search into
publications and journals regarding work with learning disabilities highlighted relevant literature by Ann Cattanach (1996), Flo Longhorn (2000), Veronica Sherborne (2001), David Thomas and Honor Wood (2003), Valerie Sinason (2010) and
Bernice Wong and Deborah Butler (2012).

However, there remained a gap in the literature regarding emotional development specific to people with learning disabilities. The publication, which began to
address the conception of a 'guide' for the emotional development of those with
learning disabilities, was *Social-Emotional Development of Students with Learning
Disabilities* by William N. Bender and Maureen E. Wall (1994). This publication
presented a model that identified 14 variables across the three domains of emotional, social and behavioural development. With so many variables, was it possible to track commonalities in development?

Stage 2: Commonalities and Tracking Emotional Development in Learning Difficulties

In 2015, the Eden Academy Trust arts therapy team had begun to work on an evaluation tool, to track emotional development and examine potential commonalities in the pupils accessing therapy. At the same time, we questioned the usefulness of comparing children with learning disabilities to the neurotypical developmental trackers. This was highlighted when delivering a multidisciplinary therapy training to education staff on 'Communication and Play'. The following statement was offered:

> Of the 70 pupils currently on roll at the school; aged 4 to 11 none of them were developmentally over the age of 18 months.

This statement had been the result of a survey carried out by a SALT assistant, who had tracked all the pupils' abilities against a government milestone checklist for 'typically' developing children. The survey concluded that there were significant gaps in developmental progress. If all milestones required 'ticking', then all the pupils in the school were far below their neurotypical peers.

Making this statement aimed to shock, to make the staff think about how they interacted with the pupils and to make them question their expectations about working with primary-aged pupils. Alongside challenging the staff's preconceptions, we welcomed arguments against this statement as staff offered examples of when a pupil's intelligence and abilities far exceeded the capabilities of an 18-month-old infant. It was concluded that the results of the survey helped us acknowledge that there were times that our interactions needed to be adapted and aimed at the pupil's emotional developmental levels. We wanted staff to understand that all

> children are born ready, able and eager to learn. They actively reach out to interact with other people, and in the world around them. Development is not an automatic process, however. It depends on each unique child having opportunities to interact in positive relationships and enabling environments.
>
> (Moylett & Stewart 2012)

Therefore, in relation to leading, developing relationships and learning through play, staff should start with where the pupil's abilities and interests lie, gathering information about their developmental abilities by observing how they naturally interacted with play objects.

Observation, playing alongside and initial interactions can give us an indication of developmental abilities. However, with a gap in the literature and commonly identified milestones being based on neurotypical development, how can we track the development of people with learning disabilities? We needed a sharper way of noting development in our pupils.

RESOS

The academy arts therapy team's 'sharper way' of measuring development had become RESOS. The intention of the RESOS framework was to record what a pupil's abilities were at the point of referral to therapy and following an initial assessment period. We researched and trialled a number of tracking and outcome measures available at the time. Various available tools were close to what we required, but none covered all our evaluation needs. The *Outcome Star* (2020) addressed topics such as the use of voice or body to communicate but did not cover the range of emotional developmental areas we needed or span the cross section from MLD to SLD. The *East Kent Outcome System* (EKOS) (Johnson & Elias 2010), popular in the National Health Service (NHS), provided a good framework for tracking but did not detail SEMH outcomes. Many other tools were based on neurotypical development. Others required clients to have a certain level of cognitive ability and provided no scope for the practitioner's observations.

Alongside the exploration of educational measurement tools, such as the Equal's Mapping and Assessing Personal Progress (MAPP) (Sissons 2010), these researched tools inspired and informed the development and pilot of the RESOS framework and SEMH report format.

The RESOS framework outlines developmental milestones under the headings of emotional development, sense of self, play and creativity and the use of voice and body. The therapist refers to a series of therapeutic aims, reasons for referral and initial observations to identify the focus of the sessions. RESOS uses a ten-step scale to identify stages of development under the above headings. For example, if we were to ask: To what extent does the child express their emotions? Point 1 would be: The pupil does not appear able to express any emotion. They do not, or are not able to, acknowledge their emotional state. Point 10 would be: The pupil is able to express a wide range of emotions congruently and in a variety of ways. They are able to acknowledge their own emotional state.

With the use of RESOS, the team have been able to develop a coherent way to track SEMH development, through the therapy process, as well as provide a common language when communicating and liaison with teaching staff.

Can a Clear Developmental Guide Be Established?

The complexity of what we tried to capture with this tool continued to develop and needed to be tested to check its 'robustness'. Despite the growing success of this tool throughout the academy, questions around commonalities remained. Bender and Wall's study (1994) took into account variables of the emotional development of people with learning disabilities, alongside the impact of the social-economic factors, personality and the institutional and support networks available. The article draws attention to the fact that there is a constant need 'to expand the marker variables or 'subject characteristics' that are measured for research populations with LD' (Bender & Wall 1994). This model has offered insight into the number of factors, which need to be considered when measuring and promoting development in children with learning disabilities. This study helped us to understand how ambitious the scope of RESOS and this research was.

I concluded that the limited, concrete research in the emotional development of children with learning disabilities was down to one simple factor: no two people with the same diagnosed disability are affected in the same way.

Not fully satisfied with this conclusion, I set out to support this hypothesis. Using Moylett and Stewart's milestone guide, I created a questionnaire to survey opinions of teachers on the developmental abilities of a cross section of pupils in the academy's schools. This established a 'tick box' exercise, asking 44 teachers, across four schools to randomly pick two pupils from their class to state whether they had the abilities outlined on the questionnaire. This gave me results for 88 pupils ranging from ages 5 through to 19 and across diagnosis of MLD and SLD. Did I hope to find a pattern or common themes? Maybe. There were many discrepancies between pupils having developed well within some areas of chronological expectations but not meeting some very early developmental milestones. It was not a surprise that a pattern could not be found with similar ages or diagnosis.

Stage 3: What Can Aid Emotional Development?

Accepting that there was no definitive way to state: 'Here are the guidelines to how children with learning disabilities develop emotionally'. I moved onto stage 3, questioning how arts therapy interventions in SEND can address disparities in emotional development and offer indicators or methods to other professionals in aiding emotional development?

This stage focused on the 20, weekly, direct one-to-one dramatherapy sessions (per client) with ten pupils. The pupils were selected using the following criteria:

- referred for arts therapy to support emotional development, understanding and or self-expression
- not currently accessing arts therapy
- not having a dual diagnosis

The research used a qualitative approach, gathering raw data by collating three sets of accounts from parents, teachers and my initial observations within dramatherapy sessions to measure the stages of emotional development for the participants.

The emotional development questionnaire, created in stage 2, was used to collect data within the initial sessions. This allowed me to identify any perceived 'gaps', potentially impacted by the learning disability, when cross referenced with typical development measures. By capturing any variances of presentation in different situations and circumstances, we could acknowledge that it is a common human feature to use a 'public face [which we] may assume both deliberately and unconsciously [and that] the form of the mask depends upon the expectations and conditioning of society, from parents, teachers, peer groups and so on' (Berry 2000, 35).

The research then incorporated RESOS to collate the referral reasons and question-naires into specific, development-focused session aims.

Session structure included ritual hello and goodbye songs, a form of check-in, an activity to encourage engagement, a period of client-led interaction, a warning of five or ten minutes left, a tidying up or saying goodbye to objects used and an activity to ground.

Structure, consistency and containment are key elements to the dramatherapy process for those with learning disabilities. They thrive best when routines are constant and often struggle with change. The dramatherapy sessions provided these key elements for participants and therefore allowed the clients to adjust to the new space and the new relationship with me.

The consistency continued through the resources available in the session, includ-ing a collection of musical instruments, objects and toys, cloths and puppets. I also relied on my 'internal' therapy tool kit of stories, the *Sesame Approach's* training of 'Movement with Touch and Sound' (Royal Central School of Speech and Drama 2020), experience of sitting with the unknown and of 'being' in the moment intui-tion and instinct and unconditional positive regard (Rogers 1967).

It is this particular set of skills which offers a unique environment for children and young people with learning disabilities to develop emotional well-being. How-ever, as a dramatherapist, I am aware of the context in which therapy takes place. For a pupil to grow, skills need to be integrated to all areas of life and not just in the therapy environment. Regular liaison with education staff and families allowed for a more informed and rounded view of the pupils and their needs. In turn, this also expanded the opportunity to identify what 'worked' for each pupil, sharing anecdotes about any progress through the stages of development, within or outside of the therapy sessions. The boundaries of information sharing are often discussed within our team. We, of course, maintain confidentiality but also take a view of ad-vocating for the pupil. Having close links with education staff is important to high-light any capabilities revealed within the therapeutic environment, which could be replicated and developed throughout their lives. This becomes a two-way sharing in order to provide the best opportunities for the pupil. Vignettes of this process, from the dramatherapy intervention, are offered below.

Debbie

Debbie is a 13-year-old girl with SLD. She is predominantly non-verbal but has learnt key words to communicate her wishes, such as saying 'more' if she wants an activity to continue.

Both Debbie's mum and class teacher commented that she rarely initiated eye contact or physical contact with adults. After two one-to-one sessions; mainly employing a mirroring method akin to Intensive Interactions (Hewett, D. & Firth, G. 2012) and incorporating 'Movement with Touch and Sound', Debbie used eye contact to get my attention. She gestured to show me what she wanted and lent her forehead against mine. Feedback to mum, which followed the session, encouraged her to find moments when they could have quiet time, just the two of them (something she struggled with due to Debbie having a SEND sibling) and being able to have brief moments of connection.

For Debbie, dramatherapy offered her the space and time she needed to be able to connect in her own unique way. She had the capability and the desire to form relationships with others but most of her life was too chaotic. In dramatherapy, we were able to stop, be quiet and wait; there were no distractions. Although difficult to find these moments in class and in her home life, being able to share my experience of Debbie in the sessions allowed other adults to note adjustments in order to form stronger connections with her.

Fred

Fred is six years old, diagnosed with autistic spectrum disorder. Most of his verbal communication stems from echolalia: repeating phrases used by adults. In familiar situations, he is able to verbally initiate interactions. Fred had been referred by class staff for concerns about his mental health and shyness in class, often seeming intimidated by other pupils. Fred's anxiety towards the unpredictable behaviour of other pupils in his class had resulted in him not being able to achieve his potential. Staff reported he was often quiet and seemed 'stuck' or 'frozen', unable to engage or interact with adults.

> Fred was cautious to begin with, looking at me every time he began to explore something new in the session, seeking reassurance that this was ok. After a few consistent sessions of encouragement he began to test boundaries: jumping on the piano; knocking over the cymbals (and enjoying my 'dramatic' reactions); directing me to move around the space or to create loud, chaotic environments. Fred's teacher was shocked to hear about his interactions and commented: 'He must think all his Christmases have come at once'. Hearing of Fred's potential to be more playful and imaginative, class staff began to reassure and encouraged him, noting, particularly in the playground, a braver and more adventurous side of his character.

Through dramatherapy, Fred used the safe, non-judgemental environment to play and test boundaries. For example, not being 'told off' for jumping on the piano, but being reminded that play could only happen, 'when we are safe' and being directed off the piano. Class staff were pleased that Fred had this space, and the knowledge of his potential encouraged them to find ways to witness it for themselves.

Sarah

Nine-year-old Sarah was referred for dramatherapy to explore the experience of her mother passing away when she was four. Her Education, Health and Care Plan (EHCP) naming MLD. School staff experienced her as vulnerable, often crying and needing comfort, but Sarah demonstrated a different side of herself in drama-therapy. Having the one-to-one attention in dramatherapy allowed her to express a need to be in control. The distancing (Landy 1986) of role-play and creating stories allowed her to take a very directive role towards me. Sarah chose not to bring to therapy her vulnerable, teary side or wish to reflect on sad events in her life.

> Following in depth discussions with the staff in the school about recent events in her life and through supervision I decided to remind her that this was a space she could share difficult things. She was avoidant at first but her play became more demanding and 'bossy' towards me. In one session I told her that her teacher was worried about her. Her play became very frantic and she wet herself. She became very ashamed. With help from a teaching assistant from her class, we got her clean clothes and she chose to return to therapy. Sarah became very angry. Through interaction with soft toys, embodiment and use of the emotion carpet (a circular rug with 12 different emotional facial expressions) Sarah was able to talk through her feelings and hint at some of her experiences.

It felt as if dramatherapy enabled distance from everyday life and reality for Sarah, a chance to have this direct attention she craved everywhere else and to be who she wanted to be. She had control over her environment, something unfamiliar in *her* real world. Although resistant to exploring her life experiences directly, the dramatherapy environment had provided her with a safe, containing place to address some of these big emotions.

Hector

Hector, 15, has a diagnosis of MLD. His receptive abilities were very good, but he struggled to be verbally coherent. Hector had become very withdrawn in class and would cry without any obvious trigger; his mum also reported similar incidents, which were 'So unlike him'.

> With advance notice, in the form of a picture of me and a dramatherapy symbol to go on his daily timetable, he was very willing to come to a dramatherapy session but seemed hesitant and unsure in initial sessions and did not speak. I liaised with class staff and with his SaLT. Hector had the ability to speak but was often incoherent and 'mumbled' to himself a lot but was able to communicate with peers and seemed to enjoy playing with dolls. I brought puppets into the session and Hector was immediately drawn to them. He began to use them to 'play out' romantic fantasies and ideas of parenthood; putting a baby shaped toy up the dress of the 'girl' puppet. His play remained silent for a few more sessions and he found it hard to respond if I offered him the opportunity to interact with my puppet. More discussions took place with teachers and the SaLT and I began to 'parallel play' (Bakeman et al 1980) alongside Hector; mirroring the way he animated the puppets, developing the interactions between my puppets

and adding in a dialogue. Hector began to copy my additions. Although his dialogue was incoherent to me, he showed great expression and I felt a real wish to connect. He was then able to accept interactions with my puppets.

Further liaison with mum and teachers revealed that he was becoming more communicative outside of the therapy session, and we all agreed that going through puberty and venturing to adulthood was affecting his emotional state. He was soon able to express in class a wish to be friends with a female pupil but that sometimes she made him feel sad.

Evaluation

As therapists employed within education, there is a need to find balance between our core principles and the need to be flexible to meet the demands and expectations of the institution. The Eden Academy Trust is in the fortunate position to be able to employ a sufficient number of therapists to meet pupil's holistic needs. However, there is demand to produce evidence of the effectivity of clinical interventions, for the cost implications of such a provision. Therapy outcome measures are required to link with class set targets. RESOS plays a crucial role in finding this balance.

Combining the RESOS process and data collected from the questionnaires allowed me to identify specific outcomes or milestones that therapy, school and home environments could jointly address. A paired down version of the questionnaire: focusing on the specific areas for each participant, were completed by myself, the parents and the teacher halfway through the dramatherapy intervention and again at the end.

Following the interim, feedback adjustments were made to therapy sessions. These included changing session times, including teaching assistants during transitions to and from the therapy space for more effective access, changing length of sessions, offering more direct interventions and activities designed to increase interaction and exploring ways to encourage shifts in stuck states of being.

At the end of the project, the collated data was analysed, showing that in therapy sessions, eight out of the ten participants made progress in identified aims; seven of these eight also reportedly made progress in the classroom or at home. When discussing the intervention with families and teachers, we established that the consistency of interactions between various adults and the pupil created greater cohesion to support their emotional development. A review into potential reasons for pupils not progressing identified the impact of variants, similar to those named by Bender and Wall (1994): absences from school, poor health, changes to family and home environments and changes in class-based staff.

Conclusion

Skills within the social and emotional domain are believed to lay a critical foundation for later life success across a wide variety of outcomes.

(Halle & Darling-Churchill 2016)

The research described in this chapter set out to establish whether there was a coherent way to track emotional development in children and young people with learning disabilities. Like Bender and Wall (1994), I have been able to conclude that there are many variances across MLD and SLD which also constantly change within a child's life. This makes formulating a 'one size fits all' model similar to that for 'typical' development challenging. Those with learning disabilities are the square pegs, and maybe, it is time that we stop trying to fit them in round holes. Labelling children and young people with learning disabilities as developmentally far lower than their chronological age needs to shift to incorporate the possibility of being at different levels across various stages of development. Having said this, my research has shown that being able to identify and track emotional development can open up the potential for pinning down how to aid those with learning difficulties develop emotionally.

This chapter highlights that liaising and facilitating regular contact with other adults in the lives of these children and young people is essential. As dramatherapists, we are often gifted with a unique view of this client group. The environment we offer allows them to 'just be'. With no expectations and an unconditional positive regard (Rogers 1967), the clients are often able to show a different side of themselves and realise their potential.

However, we are only with them for an extremely short time in their week. We therefore need to utilise those who know them best, those who stand by them in the moments of real positivity as well as moments which impact negatively. We need to advocate for this client group. In order to do that, we need to have a holistic picture of 'how' and 'who' they are in all situations.

> Until there is conscious and planned cooperation between trained analysts and psychotherapists throughout the Health and Social Services, and Arts practitioners, I cannot see how maximum benefit can be received by those in need.
>
> (Lindvist 1998)

Through this piece of research, a guide has been created for the education staff of the Eden Academy Trust, to help identify how they can promote emotional development. A training is also available to detail how they can measure and track changes through RESOS. While the ideal scenario is that a pupil attends a creative arts therapy, allowing the therapist to facilitate an individuated guide for aiding development, it is not possible for all pupils to be seen. Therefore, introducing the idea of RESOS and guides on how to aid emotional development allows general methods and interventions to be adapted for use outside of the therapy space.

References

Action for Children. 2015. *What to Expect, When? Guidance to Your Child's Learning and Development in the Early Years Foundation Stage*. Watford: Action for Children.

Bakeman, R. & Brownlee, J.R. 1980. 'The Strategic Use of Parallel Play: A Sequential Analysis'. In: *Child Development*. Volume 51, Issue 3, 873–878. Wiley Online Library.

Bender, W. & Wall, M. 1994. 'Social-Emotional Development of Students with Learning Disabilities'. In: *Learning Disability Quarterly*. Volume 17, Issue 4, 19. 1 November 1994. London: Sage Journals.

Berry, R. 2000. *Jung: A Beginner's Guide*. London: Hodder & Stoughton.

Booker, M. 2011. *Developmental Drama*. London: Jessica Kingsley Publishers.

Cattanach, A. 1996. *Drama for People with Special Needs*. London: A&C Black (Publishers) Limited.

Chesner, A. 1994. *Dramatherapy for People with Learning Disabilities*. London: Jessica Kingsley Publisher.

Chesner, A. 1998. *Group Work with Learning Disabilities*. London: Routledge.

Crimmins, P. 2006. *Drama Therapy and Storymaking in Special Education*. London: Jessica Kingsley Publisher.

Feniger-Schaal, R., Citron, A., Mittlelberg, E. & Ben Eli, Y. 2018. 'Intervention of Medical (Therapeutic) Clowns in a Kindergarten for Children with Intellectual Disability: A Case Study'. In: *International Journal of Disability, Development and Education*, 293–305 Volume 67. November 2018. London: Routledge.

Geigera, A., Shpigelmanb, C. & Feniger-Schaala, R. 2020. 'The Socio-Emotional World of Adolescents with Intellectual Disability: A Drama Therapy-Based Participatory Action Research'. In: *The Arts in Psychotherapy*. Article: 101679, Volume 70. Science Direct Online: Elsevier.

Haythorne, D. & Seymour, A. 2017. *Dramatherapy and Autism*. London: Routledge.

Halle, T.G. & Darling-Churchill, K.E. 2016. 'Review of Measures of Social and Emotional Development'. In: *Journal of Applied Developmental Psychology*. Volume 45, 8–18. July–August 2016. Science Direct Online: Elsevier.

Hewett, D. & Firth, G. 2012. *Intensive Interaction Institute: Curriculum Documents for Schools*. Puckeridge: The Intensive Interaction Institute.

Intensive Interaction Institute. 2020. https://www.intensiveinteraction.org/ Accessed: 28 October 2021.

Johnson, M. & Elias, A. 2010. *East Kent Outcome System: User Manual and Clinical Supplements;* Revised editions. NHS: Eastern and Coastal Community Services. www.choiceforum.org›docs›ekos Accessed: 28 October 2021.

Jones, P., Cedar, L., Coleman, A., Haythorne, D., Mercieca, D. & Ramsden, E. 2020. *Child Agency and Voice in Therapy: New Ways of Working in the Arts Therapies*. London: Routledge.

Karkou, V. 2010. *Arts Therapies in Schools: Research and Practice*. London: Jessica Kingsley Publishers.

Landy, R. 1986. *Drama Therapy: Concepts and Practices*. Springfield, IL: Charles C. Thomas Publisher.

Lindvist, M. 1998. *Bring White Beads When You Call on the Healer*. Memphis, TN: River House, Limited.

Longhorn, F. 2000. *Sensory Drama for Very Special People*. Copyright 2000 by Florence Longhorn.

Moylett, H. & Stewart, N. 2012. *Development Matters in the Early Years Foundation Stage (EYFS)*, produced by Early Education: The British Association for Early Childhood Education (www.early-education.org.uk) Development Matters in the Early Years Foundation Stage (2012) | Early Education (early-education.org.uk) Accessed: 28 October 2021.

Outcome Star. 2020. https://www.outcomesstar.org.uk/using-the-star/see-the-stars/music-therapy-star/ Copyright: Triangle Consulting Social Enterprise Limited, Accessed: 09 October 2021.

Payne, H. 2017. *Essentials of Dance Movement Psychotherapy: Internal Perspectives on Theory, Research and Practice*. London: Routledge.

Pearson, J. 1996. *Discovering the Self through Drama and Movement: The Sesame Approach*. London: Jessica Kingsley Publishers.

Rogers, C. 1967. *On Becoming a Person*. London: Constable and Company Ltd.

Royal Central School of Speech and Drama: https://www.cssd.ac.uk/ma-drama-movement-therapy Accessed: 28 October 2021.

Sherborne, V. 2001. *Developmental Movement for Children*. Derbyshire: Worth Publishing.

Sinason, V. 2010. *Mental Handicap and the Human Condition*. London: Free Association Books.

Sissons, M. 2010. *Mapping and Assessing Personal Progress.* Equals. https://equals.co.uk/mapp-semi-formal-mapping-and-assessing-personal-progress/ Accessed 10 October 2021.

Thomas, D. & Wood, H. 2003. *Working with People with Learning Disabilities: Theory and Practice*. London: Jessica Kingsley Publishers.

Watson, T. 2007. *Music Therapy with Adults with Learning Disabilities*. London: Routledge.

Wong, B. & Butler, L. 2012. *Learning about Learning Disabilities*. Science Direct Online: Elsevier.

Part 2

The Journey through Adolescence

Chapter 5

Meeting Maddy Where She Is

A Figurative and Literal Journey

Amee Freyone

Introduction

It is a well-known concept in the psychotherapeutic world that the therapist must figuratively 'meet a client where they are', but what could this mean and what could it look like in schools for children and young people with complex needs and learning disabilities? When offering dramatherapy for clients with learning disabilities we need to be flexible and adapt, using a dramatherapeutic critical lens to ensure how best to lift, shift, and implement its core principles. Therapy is not formulaic; one size is not intended to fit all. As Jones states, '[t]he context and paradigm in which a Dramatherapist works needs to be considered in the forming of the aims and in the way the sessions are structured or shaped' (Jones 1996).

This chapter follows the journey of my work, as part of an 'in house' therapy service within a special educational needs and disabilities (SEND) school, with a 13-year-old girl, I will refer to as Maddy. Her father consented to this piece of therapeutic work as well as its publication.

The diversity of this client group's needs requires a particularly flexible approach – the therapist's duty to meet their client 'where they are' can often be as literal as it is figurative. This work has taught me that, while many children and young people are able to access therapy by moving from class to the therapy space, there are clients who struggle with this transition. So, how do the adults around the child cooperate to create a helpful therapeutic process within their school environment? If we uphold the tradition that therapy must happen in 'the room', many children and young people in this environment will simply not access therapy. When working with an already marginalised demographic (Chesner 1995, 1), it becomes even more important for the therapist to consciously reconfigure the psychotherapeutic framework in order to make it accessible to this client group's reality. Meeting Maddy has shown me the power and potential of communication through the body in the absence of words. This chapter hopes to encourage other dramatherapists to find a way of initiating a therapeutic relationship, when being with others is what the client finds most demanding. 'In a society where [...] we find it hard to communicate with those whose verbal skills are limited' (Chesner 1995, 1),

DOI: 10.4324/9781003091783-8

dramatherapists are able to utilise the body as an integral means of communication and in the building of trust within the therapeutic work.

This chapter sheds light on the importance of being alongside the client, even if this means working in ways that defy traditional psychotherapeutic paradigms. When a child does not have the words to express why they cannot physically move themselves from classroom to therapy room, does the therapist end the process there? Surely, it is the therapist's responsibility to find a way of offering a therapeutic invitation, in a way that is more palatable to the client with learning disabilities. On this occasion, I took the therapy to the young person in their safe space – the classroom, and their safety was communicated through the body, not words. It is the therapist's task to listen with the body and offer a safe, therapeutically informed, encounter that suits the needs of those they are working with. This chapter will illustrate how a therapist may generate trust with individuals with learning disabilities non-verbally, through the shared embodied experience of togetherness and responsiveness when we are working. The client's meaning-making, sense of trust, and safety within this therapeutic context occurs viscerally, 'alongside' verbal exchanges, because words alone are not enough.

This chapter describes three separate areas of Maddy's dramatherapeutic process:

1 The lived experience of trust
2 Avenues for spontaneity
3 Integration and generalisation of therapeutically informed experiences with others

Meeting Maddy

Maddy was 13 and the eldest of five siblings aged 3–11. She had diagnoses of autism spectrum disorder (ASD) and pathological demand avoidance (PDA) and was hard to reach. Maddy would defecate and smear around the school building and screech at, or hit, children and staff if they came too close to her. Maddy had sensory processing difficulties and as a result disliked washing her hands, showering, or brushing her hair and teeth. People could not tolerate being around her, and likewise, it was difficult for her to be physically close to others; her behaviour kept others away. Being her must have been hard.

Maddy had some words. She seldom used them to communicate but seemed to block the world out with them, often deflecting demands from adults or avoiding an activity by repeating lines from television, songs, or clips she had watched online. She was referred to the arts therapy team to support her emotional expression at a time of 'significant transition through puberty, which also rendered her moody and unpredictable' (Zeal 2011, 76). The combination of adolescence; ASD; PDA; an inconsistent relationship with her mother, who was not always at home; as well as the social, emotional, and academic demands presented to her in school was at times too much for her to hold. The early teenage years are a time when the brain goes through another 'intense reorganisation' (Gerhardt 2004, 195), a time when new ways of relating could be fostered and nurtured and therefore a crucial time for therapeutic input.

Information sharing was complicated in the school. Safeguarding policies limited access to extensive information about Maddy's history, making the therapeutic process even harder to navigate. Maddy had witnessed domestic violence. The teaching team around her found it hard to manage being with her without fear of being physically targeted. Her destructive and self-isolating presentation quickly convinced me that the one aspect of her life, without a formal diagnosis, was the one that needed most thinking about. That was the trauma she had experienced at home, which had shattered her ability to trust (Van Der Kolk 2014).

Maddy's Lived Experience of Trust: Building a Relationship through Play and Movement

Working in a school alongside occupational therapists (OTs), speech and language therapists (SaLTs), physiotherapists, and other arts therapists, as part of an embedded therapeutic team, played a significant role in my therapeutic approach to Maddy. Forming positive relationships with these colleagues whose expertise lay in their respective fields informed how I was to begin meeting her. Like many children with ASD, she was comforted by her routine and visual timetable. She would attend structured daily OT sessions with a specialist teaching assistant (TA) Sue, who was employed to support the OT team. Maddy and Sue had a positive relationship, and clearly, she was the one staff member Maddy really trusted. Building on this existing relationship was one way of meeting her where she was. There are other accounts of dramatherapists using known members of staff when starting to work therapeutically, particularly in schools, and these auxiliaries prove to be an invaluable part of the therapeutic process (Chesner 1995, 15; McFarlane & Harvey 2012; Sajnani & Johnson 2014). Unfortunately, Sue went on long-term sick leave just as sessions were due to begin and was thus unavailable. I now wondered how to proceed.

Maddy was severely distressed by the mere prospect of leaving her classroom, her 'secure base' (Bowlby 1997), to take herself into a new and unfamiliar space with a strange person. It became clear that dramatherapy would simply have to come to her. '[…T]he way boundaries are dealt with varies according to the context and approach' (Jones 1996, 33), and so, the dramatherapist had to find a way of meeting Maddy in her own space.

An encounter in an empty space is the essence of theatre, according to Peter Brook, but his '[p]ure, virgin space' (Brook 1993, 4) needs to be rethought in the context of learning disabilities, as children like Maddy find new, fresh, and empty spaces frightening, intimidating, and impossible to function in. Using a clinical application of 'the therapeutic relationship' (Clarkson 2003), which involves an attentiveness to the inherent communication difficulties experienced by those with additional needs, and a sense of how trauma can affect relationships and behaviour, the therapist needs to mindfully cultivate a bespoke 'newness' for the client. This 'newness' is subtly developed within the already existing and familiar environment of the therapeutic process. Merging new activities with the client's version of sameness is particularly meaningful for those on the autistic spectrum and/or those with PDA, as it reduces uncertainty and helps to manage anxiety (The National Autistic Society 2018); familiarity, sameness, and predictability equate to comfort and/or safety and were to be key in our therapeutic work.

Having been 'repeatedly overwhelmed' and becoming 'identified with states of anxiety and helplessness' (Levine & Frederik 1997, 168), meant gaining trust and forming new bonds (Van der Kolk 2014) was challenging for Maddy. The verbal negotiation of boundaries needed to be rethought by using a method that was meaningful to her, through non-verbal processes (Jones 1996, 33). This meant establishing trust by using client-informed attunement through both the body and verbal narrative simultaneously. There was no way of starting to connect with Maddy other than by physically meeting her where she was in the school building: in her classroom.

Dramatherapy Intervention

The following descriptions are vignettes of moments that capture how the work unfolded.

The First Five Months of Work: Building Trust through Encounter

Session 1: I visited her in class when her classmates were off-site and showed her our bespoke visual (laminated printouts of pictures or photos, often used to facilitate communication and understanding in educational settings) a photo of both our faces, with symbols for dramatherapy and for the day of the week on them. It was important that she knew when to expect a visit, and this was a proven way of communicating this message. A TA was present.

Session 2: I said hello, taking an interest in what she had been drawing in class. I introduced the concept of choosing in dramatherapy, saying, 'You can say yes or no' when offering her an idea. She threw our visuals off the table. I told her it felt like she was telling me 'No', so I picked it up, said goodbye but told her I would be back to see her next week.

Session 3: She looked at me as I walked into the room. I asked if I could sit next to her, reminding her she could 'say yes or no'. She nodded 'Mhm'. I sat next to her. The TA in the room widened her eyes and shook her head at me, as if to question what I was doing. It was a clear communication that they did not trust Maddy, so it felt important for me to model the part of the trusting adult so as to nurture her own self-esteem and confidence (Chesner 1995, 41). I held a mirror in front of us, so that we were looking at one another through it. She smiled at me and said 'Hello'. It was the first time we had made eye contact. Maddy leaned in my direction. She offered a relaxed and playful energy that I matched by mirroring her facial expression, body language, and playfully naming what was happening (Winnicott 1971, 47–48). Therapist: 'I see you looking at me! Maddy is looking at me. We are close and staying safe'. I pointed at a visual representing our working together. It had a 'safe' symbol on it, to remind us of what the feeling was called when we were mutually experiencing a feeling of safety or security in each other's company. I gently slid the visual along the table until it was in front of her, pointing at the 'safe' symbol and repeatedly naming it. For a while, we were immersed in its immediacy. This sequence of actions was to be played out repeatedly throughout the first five months.

Significant Moments of Change for Maddy

Maddy occasionally looked at the 'safe' symbol, sometimes pushing it away, but she began repeating the word 'safe' when she was calm, regulated, and connected to the therapist in the space. These moments of stillness gave rise to fun, energising and playful interactions (Chesner 1995, 54–55), it involved 'hand to hand conversation' (Chesner 1995, 40), pushing against one another's shoulders, and singing the hello and goodbye song together.

Maddy once raised her hand, feigning to hit me:

Therapist: I wonder if I'm too close? You can tell me: 'You're too close' and I will move, like this (therapist shuffles chair away from Maddy)
Maddy: Too close
Therapist: Okay, I'm moving (shuffles chair away). Is this okay with you?
Maddy: Mhm (nodding and watching closely)

After some months, Maddy hugged me, placing her cheek on mine, holding my face, and looking into my eyes. I smiled at her once again and reminded her we could be 'close and safe'.

This approach enabled the deliberate yet organic creation of the 'client-therapist Shared Language' (Chesner 1995, 77). This process of embodying a sense of safety and placing it at the forefront of the therapeutic work, to forge a positive relationship with Maddy so that we could share a space together, reminded me of the significance of the client's perception of safety in Porges' 'Polyvagal Theory' (2011). It is the client's consistent need to feel safe in the therapeutic environment that Porges says is vital in order to support the client's 'social engagement system'; this safety enables 'social bonds' and avoids triggering the fight-or-flight response (2011). Van der Kolk echoes this notion, telling us that 'social relationships [are at the] front and centre in our understanding of trauma' (2014, 78). I had met Maddy socially, in a place that was familiar to her, and presented myself in the least threatening manner I could. Ultimately, 'one is not bound by unity of place, a unity of time, when emphasis is on human relationships' (Brook 1993, 29). The latter was at the core of Maddy's difficulties and therefore where the centre of the therapeutic work lay.

The centrality of a lived, visceral togetherness between therapist and client is also echoed in concepts in trauma recovery literature. Renegotiation and alignment (Levine & Frederik 1997, 199, 204), physical mirroring and 'microtracking' (Van der Kolk 2014, 58–59, 297), and the NeuroAffective Relational Model (NARM) model (Heller & LaPierre 2012, 20–21), alongside the therapist's live narration, are some of the notable key approaches to cultivating positive connection, reparative re-experiencing, and therefore healing. In movement psychotherapy, Bloom refers to this as 'embodied attentiveness' (2006, 65). It focuses the attention on the 'sensoriaffective realm', forming the basis of 'primitive communication' (Bloom 2006, 65). These processes allow the client to be immersed in a lived experience of congruence. The immersion in positive embodied experience is in and of itself reparative for the client (Jennings 2011, 19).

In this way, the therapist (much like a mother for her baby) acts as the 'sole container' for the client, as it is only through their evolving relationship, and its lived simulation, that the 'healing' begins. Maddy's presentation and my chosen approach with her drew my attention to the links between ASD, PDA, and trauma, and how we can use these connections to inform our practice when working with children and young people with learning disabilities. I am suggesting that the overlap between ASD, PDA, and experiences of trauma lie in the individual's feelings of anxiety, their need for sameness, and their search for familiarity.

Sameness and familiarity were not consistent in Maddy's home life. Towards the end of our first block of therapy, at the end of the academic year, Maddy came into school with her front two teeth broken. Upon speaking with the safeguarding team, I learnt she had been in a traffic accident with her mother, who was an alcoholic and drink driving at the time of the crash. Maddy's mother was no longer allowed to see her and had moved out of the family home, leaving Maddy in her father's care.

Developing Spontaneity

Returning in the new academic year provided another opportunity for Maddy to build upon what we had established before the summer holidays. Her OT and I came together and decided that we could facilitate joint sessions as our therapeutic aims overlapped. From the OT's perspective, Maddy needed support with self-care skills, building muscle tone, and self-regulation. Sue, the specialised OT TA, was now back at work and was able to invite Maddy to attend a weekly session outside her classroom, in a purpose-built room. There, she would follow a ritualised visual timetable (that she would place into the 'finish box' each time she completed an activity), and here, in a contained and structured environment, she was able to re-experience her body in ways that were safe.

Joint dramatherapy and occupational therapy sessions began:

> Maddy would guzzle her food in the school dining hall and run straight to the therapy space. For safety, the four of us (OT, TA, Sue, and myself) would sit and wait for her to finish her lunch, sometimes taking it in turns to sit with her while

she ate, then following her lead when she was ready. Although there was no set session time, it was always straight after lunch.

The sessions were structured as follows:

- Shoes off
- Hello song sitting in a circle: opportunity to play the drum
- Check-in with feeling faces: foam masks showing a range of feelings used to help label and bring more explicit awareness to emotions
- Followed by three to four OT activities ranging from:

  - Rolling on the peanut ball to build muscle tone
  - Crawling through a tunnel to develop gross motor skills
  - Brushing teeth
  - Washing hands
  - Brushing hair
  - Swinging (vestibular input; an occupational therapy term used to describe 'slow rhythmic swinging movement stimulation' intended to be calming; NHS 2020, 8)
  - Maddy choosing what animals she could reach and pick up off the floor while on the swing for fine motor skill development

- One or two creative expressive activities:

  - By using the 'choosing' visual, she was given two creative options to choose from (for example, 'drawing or puppets')
  - Playing with lycra: pulling and pushing (Chesner 1995, 44–45)
  - Finger painting: appealing to her tactile needs and then giving her another opportunity to wash her hands

- Always ending with:

  - Singing the goodbye song in a circle

  - Shoes on and walking back to class

Examples of Moments of Change

When Maddy was close and connected with the therapist:

- Maddy asked for 'deep pressure' by requesting hugs from the adults in the room, seeking out touch in a healthy and safe way. OTs refer to this as 'proprioceptive feedback'; proprioception is about our 'movement and body position' as perceived by our 'internal eyes', which help inform where we are in space (NHS 2020, 8)
- Holding the therapist's face right in front of hers and looking closely, smiling, she kissed the therapist's face, saying, 'You are a hero – I am a girl, I am a sister'

- Therapist took her dried finger painting from an earlier session into her classroom – she said, 'Thank you' and smiled at the therapist
- Laughter together

Maddy was able to engage in and offer more while in the space:

- Engaging in deep breathing, physical relaxation, tug of war while seated with fabric – smiling and connected
- Brushing teeth
- Being spontaneous: trying out and attending to new materials/activities
- The beginnings of stories being told
- Maddy's ability to communicate her sense of self and her wishes (Haythorne & Seymour 2017, 10)

Maddy was able to reflect in ways that were congruent:

- Showing empathy when OT was off sick, saying, 'Oh no, poor Lily'
- Maddy once requested to go back to the therapy space following a fire alarm evacuation
- Able to tolerate increasing time spent in the room and with the number of different activities
- Observing a verbal boundary or reminder to stay safe when she feigned hitting me

It was only when Maddy was able to experience long-term embodied safety that she was able to be still and regulated. The foundations of trust that enabled her to be in a room with another were a fundamental part of the second stage of her therapeutic process. Simply being in the company of another without feeling under threat cultivated a sense of presence, calm, and silence. Brook's theatre-making processes also informed encounters between Maddy and myself. Brook's primary focus is on the actors themselves, the quality of the communication between them, and their relationships with one another (1993). This practice nurtures trust, which for Maddy meant experiencing stillness, and it was through the practice of stillness or 'emptiness' *within the lived relationship,* that Maddy's 'imagination [was able] to fill the gaps' (Brook 1993, 27), and she discovered she had the capacity to play.

Maddy had attended 19 sessions and was in the middle of an OT activity, when she suddenly got up and ran out of the room. She came to a locked door and lay on the floor saying, 'I don't like therapy anymore'. I wondered whether she felt overwhelmed, threatened by, or unsafe with, the number of staff in the room, and I reminded her that this was okay, because 'Remember, you can choose – you can say yes and you can say no'. Sue helped Maddy put her shoes back on and accompanied her back to class. Maddy then declined sessions for three months, during which time she became increasingly fixated with her electronic tablet and, as a result, declined to take part in class-based activities with her peers. I wondered if she might have been processing significant events from the past, or that perhaps, even if unconsciously, Maddy was responding to an anniversary of a traumatic event, of which there need not be any conscious memory (Levine & Frederik 1997, 185).

Aside from overtly illustrating the dramatherapy paradigm, wherein rituals give rise to spontaneity (Jones 1996), Maddy's joint OT and dramatherapy sessions exemplified therapists' ability to embody a way of being that follows the client's lead. If Maddy sought to be close, that is what we offered her. She had been separated from her mother, so providing her opportunities for closeness, especially with individuals who possibly represented the mother in the transference relationship (Clarkson 2003, 67), was a way of repairing the mother/child attachment and/or her internal sense of mother. This was central in Maddy's therapeutic process, as her efforts to connect can be read as 'attempts to restore closeness to the mother' and 'it is only when the mother is accessible and available that her child can turn his or her attention to the rest of the world' (Ruppert 2015, 51).

Therapy being child led is key within an educational context, where demands and routines are often imposed on children, by which their autonomy is compromised. Jordan and Powell echo this notion and suggest that by not following the child's need, the therapist is imposing their own agenda on the child (1995, 22). This rationale validated Maddy's self-directed extended hiatus from therapy.

Integration and Generalisation

As the end of the academic year coincided with my leaving the school, and after three months of her declining therapy, it felt important to mark our goodbye. Maddy had developed a strong attachment to her electronic tablet, playing games and re-watching the same cartoons repeatedly. The staff team around her explained that it was impossible to get her to do any work because of her preoccupation with the screen and difficulty connecting with anything or anyone beyond it. The safeguarding team reported Maddy knew her mother was visiting her siblings but not her. Her struggles surrounding this situation, alongside my leaving the academy, were the basis for her final block of therapeutic work. Once again, this was offered to her in her classroom and Maddy willingly engaged. This time, there needed to be a 'handover' of our way of being to her classroom teacher, who would continue to work with her at school in the following academic year. It is the dramatherapist's duty to pass on ideas, approaches, and modes of being to other professionals working with the child. We proposed the teacher's presence in sessions to facilitate their understanding of how to be with, and respond to, Maddy in ways that were nurturing and meaningful. I hoped this therapeutic framework would offer Maddy a clear, contained, and good-enough ending.

I visited her in class with Pete, her teacher, for her last session of dramatherapy. Again, we timed this so that her classmates were off-site. She was watching her tablet and only occasionally glanced up at me as we sang the hello song. It felt important not to remove the tablet from her, as it felt like her way of keeping herself safe. The transitional object is, after all, a defence against anxiety (Winnicott 1971, 4), enabling the infant to cope with the absence of the internal mother and defend the complete control of the infant (Winnicott 1971, 23–24). Like the good-enough mother, who allows the infant to exercise their need to control through the transitional object (McAlister 2011, 149), Pete and I modelled finger painting next to her, as something she had enjoyed in the past. Eventually, Maddy turned away from her screen and engaged in the art. Artwork, analogous to the transitional object (McAlister 2011, 149), is pacifying and facilitates connection through shared experience.

The following weeks took a sudden turn. Maddy spontaneously started engaging with figurines, repeatedly bringing up themes of love and partnership. She picked up the king figurine and said, 'Where is the queen? The mum?' I replied, 'The mum is not here – that's hard', drawing an ambiguous-enough parallel between her play and her own life. She made eye contact with me. At the end of the session, when counting down how much time we had left, she became upset, shouting 'Ah' and 'No!'. When I acknowledged it was 'hard to say goodbye', she was able to put the figurines away. Each week, Maddy was able to ignore her tablet that sat on the table. It was more important to attend to the positive events happening in the space, instead of trying to get her put the tablet away. Maddy became able to voice and exercise a choice when offered an invitation. The development of stories and a consequent transformation of implicit memory to explicit memory (Siegel & Payne Bryson 2012, 76–77), as well as her newfound capacity to verbalise her wishes, were other significant developments in her therapeutic process. Maddy's presentation suggested she was no longer living in the fight-flight-freeze response state (Siegel & Payne Bryson 2012, 129). The final phase of her work served to illustrate that sharing the therapeutic space with other appropriate professionals can be an effective way of skill-sharing and training wider school staff. Such class-based interventions allow the therapist to model an alternative way of fostering trust, safety, and 'being' that school staff might later emulate outside the therapeutic hour/session.

Conclusion

Bringing attention to the parallels (feelings of anxiety and comfort in sameness) between ASD, PDA, and the effects of trauma, this chapter has endeavoured to re-frame the way dramatherapists can consider setting up new work with children and young people with learning disabilities in a SEND school environment. Through the case study presented in this chapter, we are able to draw links between the therapeutic focus of PDA, trauma, and the therapist's awareness of 'trust, grounding, holding, nurture and senses' (Chesner 1995, 9), that is required in therapeutic working with learning disabilities. Gaining trust in one's own body is the first step towards profound change. This chapter hopes to serve as a reminder that the most rudimentary human reparation lies in connecting with others through meaningful relationships. If this means physically taking the therapy to the child, it is our duty as creative arts therapists to do just that. Using our clinical judgement to decipher how we reintegrate the healthy parts of the client may mean seeing them, even if only briefly, outside a clearly defined therapy space. At first, we must meet individuals with learning disabilities where they are, figuratively and otherwise, in order to nurture meaningful connections. The dramatherapist working in collaboration with other school staff is a significant facilitator of therapeutic work, as long as their approach and engagement remains always unwavering and predictable.

In light of what Maddy taught me, I hope this chapter helps other dramatherapists working in schools and looking for a way into the extraordinarily spontaneous nature of people with learning disabilities. It reiterates the significance of the *embodied experience* of trust, safety, and nurture, using first-hand experiences of working with children and young people with ASD and PDA and merging this understanding with trauma-informed therapy practices. Chesner alludes to the flexibility of the therapeutic space when working with profound learning disability, drawing attention to the need to 'give the client the spatial conditions he or she prefers' (1995, 36). Maddy's process fortifies the notion that therapeutic 'space' need not be so rigidly defined with this client group; 'the dramatherapist herself becomes a "play object" and uses her own playfulness and engagement with the client's material as the vehicle for facilitation' (Dokter et al 2011, 189).

References

Autism Speaks Inc. 2020. *Autism Diagnosis Criteria: DMS-5.* Available at: https://www.autismspeaks.org/autism-diagnosis-criteria-dsm-5 (Accessed May 2020).
Bloom, K. 2006. *The Embodied Self, Movement and Psychoanalysis.* London: Karnac Books.
Bowlby, J. 1997. *Attachment and Loss.* London: Pimlico.
Brook, P. 1993. *There Are No Secrets: Thoughts on Acting and Theatre.* London: Bloomsbury.
Chesner, A. 1995. *Dramatherapy for People with Learning Disabilities.* London: Jessica Kingsley Publishers.
Clarkson, P. 2003. *The Therapeutic Relationship.* London: Whurr Publishers.
Dokter, D., Holloway, P., & Seebohm, H. eds. 2011. *Dramatherapy and Destructiveness: Creating the Evidence Base, Playing with Thanatos.* East Sussex: Routledge.
Gerhardt, S. 2004. *Why Love Matters.* East Sussex: Routledge.
Haythorne, D. & Seymour, A. eds. 2017. *Dramatherapy and Autism.* Oxon: Routledge.
Heller, L. & Lapierre, A. 2012. *Healing Developmental Trauma.* Berkeley, CA: North Atlantic Books, U.S.
Jennings, S. 2011. *Healthy Attachments and Neuro-Dramatic Play.* London: Jessica Kingsley Publishers.
Jones, P. 1996. *Drama as Therapy: Theatre as Living.* London: Routledge.
Jordan, R. & Powell, S. 1995. *Understanding and Teaching Children with Autism.* Chichester: John Wiley and Sons Ltd.
Levine, P.A. & Frederik, A. 1997. *Waking the Tiger: Healing Trauma.* Berkeley, CA: North Atlantic Books.
McAlister, M. 2011. 'From transitional object to symbol: Spiderman in a dramatherapy group with mentally disordered offenders.' In: Dokter, D., Holloway, P., & Seebohm,

H. eds. *Dramatherapy and Destructiveness: Creating the Evidence Base, Playing with Thanatos*, 145–156. East Sussex: Routledge.

McFarlane, P. & Harvey, J. 2012. *Dramatherapy and Family Therapy in Education*. London: Jessica Kingsley Publishers.

NHS. 2020. *Sensory Processing Dysfunction*. [online] Available at: https://www.pat.nhs.uk/community-services/PC-leaflets/Occ-therapy/ot-pre-referral-advice-for-schools-sensory.pdf (Accessed September 2021).

Porges, S. 2011. *The Polyvagal Theory*. New York: Norton.

Ruppert, F. 2015. *Trauma Fear and Love: How the Constellation of the Intention Supports Healthy Autonomy*. Trudoxhill: Green Balloon Publishing.

Sajnani, N. & Johnson, D.R. 2014. *Trauma-Informed Drama Therapy: Transforming Clinics, Classrooms, and Communities.* Springfield, IL: Charles C. Thomas, Publisher, Ltd.

Siegel, D.J. & Payne Bryson, T. 2012. *The Whole-Brain Child: 12 Revolutionary Strategies to Nurture Your Child's Developing Mind*. New York: Bantam Books.

The National Autistic Society. 2018. *About Autism.* Available at: https://www.autism.org.uk/about.aspx (Accessed May 2020).

Van Der Kolk, B. 2014. *The Body Keeps the Score: Brain, Mind and Body in the Healing of Trauma*. New York: Penguin.

Winnicott, D.W. 1971. *Playing and Reality*. London: Routledge.

Zeal, E. 2011. 'Chaos, destruction and abuse: Dramatherapy in a school for excluded adolescents.' In: Dokter, D., Holloway, P. & Seebohm, H. eds. *Dramatherapy and Destructiveness: Creating the Evidence Base, Playing with Thanatos*, 66–77. East Sussex: Routledge.

Chapter 6

The Hero's Journey and Learning Disability

A Case Study

Rosalind Davidson

Introduction

This chapter has derived from my work in a Special Needs Secondary school, offering long-term, one-to-one interventions to a range of young people with moderate learning disabilities (MLD), autistic spectrum disorder (ASD), looked after children (LAC) and those who have a high number of adverse childhood experiences (ACEs). I work as part of the Wellbeing and Emotional Support team (WEST) which is led by the Designated Safeguarding Lead and comprises student support, emotional literacy support assistants (ELSA), dramatherapy, art therapy and transactional analysis sessions. There is an ethos within the team of the importance of understanding the social and emotional needs of each individual student; this informs the alignment of the appropriate intervention to the specific needs of the young person. There is a culture of reflective practice within the team where perspectives from differing modalities are considered, shared and reviewed in order to address the complex and ever-changing needs of the students.

This chapter demonstrates the possibility for clients with learning disabilities to access a working structure that allows them to address their own emotional difficulties or traumas. This supports them to move beyond the immediate difficulties inherent in their learning disability. Young people with learning disabilities often 'find themselves on the margins of society by virtue of their difference' (Chesner 1995, 4). It is important to recognise that people with learning disabilities are also impacted by emotional difficulties and often experience challenging or traumatic life events and so should be offered a way of managing and working through these feelings.

The Hero's Journey, as set out by Paul Rebillot in *The Call to Adventure* (1993), was modelled on the teachings of Joseph Campbell, well known for his work in comparative mythology.

> Analyzing a broad spectrum of myths from different parts of the world, Campbell discovered that they all contained variations on one universal theme, one archetypal formula. This 'monomyth' as he called it, seemed to appear in all cultures and all historical periods.
>
> (Rebillot 1993, 8)

DOI: 10.4324/9781003091783-9

The monomyth follows a pattern through all cultures; a hero is called to adventure and sets out on a dangerous journey. After surmounting a series of challenges and ordeals, the hero returns healed or transformed and can use their new skills to help others. Rebillot realised the innately therapeutic possibilities inherent in the monomyth, and it forms the basis of the Hero's Journey. The process of the Hero's Journey allows the client the opportunity to connect with the core strengths of the 'hero', as well as integrating the shadow aspects of the 'demon'. We can reframe thoughts and experiences, and the reframing can help us in gaining self-awareness and perspective for ourselves and for others.

During my training in dramatherapy at Roehampton University, the Hero's Journey formed a pivotal moment in my own transformation, both personally and as a trainee dramatherapist. I discovered that the Hero's Journey (capitalised the exercise throughout) provided an opportunity to work with archetypes and symbols that exist within us all and connect with elements that intrinsically make us human. By engaging with the Hero's Journey, I was able to make meaningful changes in my own personal and professional process. As the Hero's Journey had offered me so much, it came to mind as an intervention when working with Jeremiah.

Jeremiah

Jeremiah's therapy commenced when he was 13 years old. He has a diagnosis of MLD, ASD and attention-deficit hyperactivity disorder (ADHD). He was initially referred for dramatherapy due to difficulties in forming relationships and under-standing social situations. There had been an increase in altercations with peers at school, and he was struggling to manage outbursts of angry feelings. The case study vignettes in this chapter reflect the Jeremiah's journey as he explored his own complex relationships and his difficulties with *Theory of Mind* (Baron-Cohen 2008): the ability to understand and recognise the emotional states, behaviours and attitudes of others. Jeremiah had already attended 25 sessions of dramatherapy when we began our work on the Hero's Journey. He had an immediate and power-ful connection to dramatherapy and had demonstrated creativity and a connection to working through metaphor and story. Jeremiah had begun to make clear connec-tions between the metaphorical work and his real life. I believed that the Hero's Journey could offer Jeremiah a contained way in which to progress more deeply into his therapeutic process.

I created a simplified version of Rebillot's Hero's Journey, based around the knowledge I had already assimilated of Jeremiah's method of working, with the aim of making the process more accessible to him. We had reached a point in our work together where we had developed a strong client/therapist relationship and Jeremiah had a good understanding of dramatherapy and the support it could offer him in everyday life. Jeremiah had verbalised his wish to change aspects of his life and was at a point where he longed to meet someone who was 'like him'. He had difficulties in making and retaining friendships and often spoke of feeling lonely. The Hero's Journey took place over a further 25 sessions.

This chapter highlights the holding elements that supported him to explore at a deep level his own personal conflicts. Through the process of the intervention, I describe how Jeremiah discovered his own strengths and experienced a form of transformation. The client's voice is a vital component in our understanding and development of dramatherapy processes. By involving children and young people directly in the research, we can potentially enhance our understanding of how we can support their growth and development (Christensen 2010). In writing this chapter, I intended for it to be as collaborative with Jeremiah as possible, and I wanted his voice to be heard throughout. This chapter concludes with an interview with Jeremiah, where he describes in his own words the impact of the Hero's Journey upon his personal process. I have also imbedded verbatim quotes from sessions and have used images that he has drawn. While the verbatim voice of Jeremiah is heard in the interview and quotes, it is through these pictures that Jeremiah really wanted his voice to be heard.

Vignette 1: The Homeground and Spirit Guide

See Figure 6.1

> …the first encounter of the hero-journey is with a protective figure.
>
> (Campbell 2008, 57)

Figure 6.1 The homeground and the spirit guide.

I invited Jeremiah to enter into the process of the Hero's Journey with me. He accepted this readily. I described to him the concept of the 'Homeground'; a place where the Hero comes from and will return to after the journey has concluded. I played him a variety of different music, and he selected a song that he felt represented his 'Homeground'. As he listened, he started to draw a picture of his 'Homeground'. He placed this in the jungle, 'the home of a poor family who had lived there for generations. The weather goes from hot sunshine to storms'. I invited Jeremiah to physically respond to the music he had chosen and to eventually create a 'sculpt', a non-verbal physical expression, of his 'Homeground'. This was a process we had worked with together in previous sessions, and Jeremiah found moving to music helped him to physically engage with and embody the characters.

We discussed the concept of the 'Spirit Guide' or 'Protective figure' that might be called on during the journey. He created a character called 'King Loowshimpee' who is the Hero's six times great grandfather. It was important to Jeremiah that he came from a wealthy family in contrast to the Hero's present poverty. He decided that he would come to the Hero in the form of a spirit or ghost. In the following session, Jeremiah created a background story for the spirit guide. I acted as scribe to his story, he then found a physical expression of the role to music, ending in another sculpt.

> 'A hundred years ago there was a great king called King Loowshimpee, who had a magical amulet that gave him powers beyond your wildest dreams. He had the power of water, where he could control it in any way he wanted. However, there were others who also had powers … Most of them were happy with the Water King, but there were two who were not happy with him and they betrayed him'.

In session 3, Jeremiah further explored a meeting between King Loowshimpee and the Hero. He explained why the Hero had not inherited the throne and why he had been raised with no knowledge of his family's past. King Loowshimpee had been murdered and:

> 'Over time the offspring of the once Water King and the Moon Queen became poorer and poorer. They became farmers and then were taken into slavery. The once royal parents had told them to never speak of their royal blood again, so as the generations went on they did not know where they had come from and they did not know of the powers he had'.

Reflection on Vignette 1

Throughout previous dramatherapy sessions and through the Hero's Journey, it became clear that Jeremiah was deeply interested in the father/son relationship and dynamic. His stories were always driven by an exploration of different male family relationships from grandfathers to uncles and brothers, and how these relationships affected the personality and behaviour of the sons. The Hero in this situation had been intentionally protected from knowledge of the men in his past family history, and discovering more about the male line of his family was one of the driving forces of his journey.

Jeremiah's personal struggles seemed to derive from a lack of knowledge about, and a feeling of 'betrayal' by, his birth father. As he understood it, his birth father had left his mum when she was pregnant, and Jeremiah had been raised by his mum and maternal grandfather. He regularly explored metaphorically, and progressively questioned consciously, how much of his personality and character had evolved from the genetics of a man who was unknown to him. It seemed that the character of King Loowshimpee held the 'wise and knowing' aspects of his family history that he longed for.

> The Spirit Guide is the representative of the individuated self and is there to help in the accomplishment of that individuation.
>
> (Rebillot 1993, 53)

Vignette 2: The Hero

Figure 6.2 The hero.

See Figure 6.2

I invited Jeremiah to begin his exploration into the Hero. He chose some important people in his life (Mum, Grandad and Batman) and explored their heroic
qualities: being loving, respectful, giving people hope, brave, funny and kind.
The Hero was named Fulooko; he was an 18-year-old boy who was kind and
gave hope to people. He had joined the revolution and stole from the rich to give
to the poor. Fulooko's parents were part of the 'Slave foundation'. Jeremiah
explained that 'he thought what his parents were doing was wrong, so he joined
the revolution and moved out of his parents' house'. Jeremiah was exploring the
idea that Fulooko had parents who were 'evil' and that he had disagreed with the
way that they led their lives.

Reflection of Vignette 2

Jeremiah struggled with whether it was 'wrong' that he wanted his hero to have
evil parents; he frequently asked for validation and permission to explore these
darker elements. He wanted to explore whether the impact of parental influence
was the key to personality. As someone who did not know his father, was his father
automatically a part of him due to his genetics? Could he reject who he thought his
father was, in order to pursue an entirely different path? The Hero was robust and
resilient, and although his parents had chosen a self-serving and evil path, Fulooko
had the possibility to choose his own fate and to follow his own beliefs. Throughout the journey, Jeremiah strongly identified with Fulooko, and through this role,
he explored the idea of making his own choices, whether they corresponded to
parental choices or not.

Jeremiah had shared during 'check-in' that a family friend had recently died.
He had discussed his wish to not attend the funeral. Jeremiah was aware that he
was not responding to his grief in a way that society counts as 'normal' and that
he had his own way of managing his grief. It had highlighted for Jeremiah his
increasing sense of being 'different' and of experiencing things 'differently' to
other people. Since starting dramatherapy sessions, Jeremiah had been developing
a deeper understanding of his autism and MLD and how that impacted on his ability to understand other people and for them to understand him. The Hero's Journey
was offering Jeremiah the vehicle through which to explore what it would be like
to do things his own way and to not have to conform to what he is 'supposed' to
do and feel.

Vignette 3: The Demons

Figure 6.3 The demons.

See Figure 6.3

'The Demon is an essential part of the whole person and cannot simply be done away with or ignored in order to satisfy the aspirations of the hero' (Rebillot 1993, 53).

> Jeremiah began this process by drawing a picture; he quickly decided that there were two demons and that they were working together. He considered whether one of the demons would be a woman disguised as a man. She would be on the Hero's 'team' as a double agent. The male demon was named Shrayth and Jeremiah redesigned an action man doll to create the character of Shrayth. He described Shrayth as having been sold by his family into the slave trade when he was a baby. When he was older, he had enlisted in the military. He had then married a member of the Royal family but he had a 'dark heart'.
>
> During session 6, Jeremiah took on the voice of Shrayth and placed me in the role of 'questioner' or 'audience'. In the role, he described how he had stolen a little girl and that initially he was going to 'punish her' and make her experience

the same terrible things that he (Shrayth) had as a child. He explained that he did not want to feel alone in his experiences. As the scene progressed, Shrayth decided instead to adopt the girl and care for her as he wished he had been cared for as a child.

Reflection of Vignette 3

Jeremiah would regularly bring to the therapy room incidents that had taken place at school or at home and that he wanted to reflect on and to unpick his own behaviour, using me, the therapist, as a sounding board for his reflections. In session 6, Jeremiah had asked me if I thought that he was 'wrong' in the way that he behaved. We had already discussed that he finds it difficult to see things from other people's perspectives and to understand their motives. Jeremiah reflected that this was really hard for him, but that he is 'getting better at it'.

Using the same model of reflecting, Jeremiah wanted to discuss whether I (as the 'audience' or 'witness') felt that Shrayth was evil or not, and whether I felt sympathy for him because of his terrible upbringing. The role of witness provided an opportunity for an emotional engagement with Jeremiah's journey. In this role, I was able to act as a receptacle for his images and thoughts (Johnson 1994). The therapeutic alliance provides space for the projections of the client and Jeremiah often placed me in this role during his sessions. Working in this way, he could take time to examine and unpick the characters' complex personalities and behaviours. This enabled him to engage with his own *Theory of Mind* to work out the motivations of their actions and to understand where their behaviours and attitudes had come from. This became a skill, that with practice, he managed to transfer from the therapy room into his own life, as he became more adept at understanding why people (even those who he did not get on with) behaved as they did.

Vignette 4: The Call to Adventure

In session 8, Jeremiah selected a 'task' or 'Call to Adventure' for the Hero. He was to collect all of the relics owned by the powerful kings and queens in the time of King Loowshimpee. Jeremiah created an embodied movement piece to begin his journey, exploring the Hero preparing himself for the task that lay ahead. He then entered into a dialogue between King Loowshimpee and the Hero, Fulooko; he switched between the two roles as he did this. The task became set that Fulooko needed to collect the relics before Shrayth did, 'as in the hands of good they will bring peace and in the hands of evil they will bring the end of life as we know it'.

Fulooko set out on his journey to get the first of the relics, The 'Moon Spear'. Jeremiah set up a battleground between the slavers and the rebels (of which Fulooko was one). He used small figures to represent the characters and entered into projective play to act out the story. A battle ensued. Jeremiah repeatedly referred to the 'bad guy' as being a 'monster' and behaving 'monstrously'. The hero had to battle hard, and it often looked as if he would lose as those around him fell in battle. The 'bad guys' imprisoned a small girl and killed her parents. When the hero eventually won, he 'adopted' the little girl.

Reflection of Vignette 4

During the check-in for session 8, Jeremiah had spoken about how he was '*trying not to rise to it*' when other students teased him. He had tried instead to speak to a teacher, rather than exploding and ending up in physical altercations. He referred to a conversation he had had with a teacher, where he had been asked to think about what his future would be like if he continued behaving in the same way. Jeremiah had interpreted this as the teacher thinking that he would become a 'monster' 'like the people you see on the telly, the murderers and all that'. Jeremiah spoke about being haunted when trying to go to sleep with questions around whether he is a monster or not.

Through the work on the Hero's Journey, Jeremiah was able to explore what he felt constituted a 'monster' and what it meant to him, to behave 'monstrously'. He was able to explore those characteristics from many different perspectives. At this point in the process, Jeremiah was able to bring his feelings to a more conscious level. He spoke at length about the difficulties he was having in making sense of the way his father had behaved towards him. He described feeling angry and rejected by his father 'abandoning' him, and yet he so desperately wanted to build a relationship with him. Jeremiah had also questioned whether his father had behaved 'monstrously' towards him by leaving when he was so young. By fully exploring the role of the 'monster', he was able to acknowledge the complex situation which led to his father not staying with him and that this decision alone did not inherently make his father a monster.

Vignette 5: The Ordeal

By session 16, Jeremiah was deeply engaged in the process of the Hero's Journey and had started to uncover characteristics of his Hero, which were not always 'heroic' and aspects of the demon's character that were not always 'evil'. During this session, Jeremiah poured a lot of water into the sand tray to make the sand very wet. Using action dolls to represent the characters, he played out a story where two brothers were trying to steal one of the relics. As the story progressed, the Hero had to make a conscious decision to take the life of one of the brothers. As this, creative, part of the session drew to a close, both brothers were dying under layers of sand as they were turned into stone.

In session 17, this exploration continued, as the Hero was thrown into a pit of lava and quick sand. He managed to use the powers that he had gained to escape. A young girl was then threatened to be thrown into the pit unless the Hero relinquished his powers. He chose to give up his powers in order to save the life of the young girl.

Reflections of Vignette 5

This seemed to be an important part of Jeremiah's process of integration of his own aspects of self. He had started to explore the complexities of his own feelings and examine the idea that he is not just one thing or another, that he is a multifaceted and complex person and that feelings and experiences can be multilayered. Through the process of the journey, the characters started to move more and more towards an experience of 'balance' and what it means to find equilibrium within yourself and the way that you behave. Jeremiah was able to reflect that,

> Much of the story is now focused on trying to find the 'balance'. Focusing too much on good or too much on evil is not successful – in order to move forward a balance needs to be found between good and evil.

As his journey progressed, Jeremiah became more consciously able to connect his experiences within the work with his own life. The process of exploring both the Hero and the demon characters (and all the other characters in the story) enabled him to look at the situations that arose from a multitude of viewpoints. He began to reflect on his own 'real life' experiences in a similar way. Working with the symbols and archetypes, inherent in his Hero's Journey, it became clear that the symbolic work was acting as a 'bridge' between the conscious and unconscious mind allowing a transformation to occur. The integration of that which comes out of the unconscious can 'contribute to a greater wholeness' (Watts 1994 p. 44).

Vignette 6: Returning

See Figure 6.4

> By session 25, Jeremiah was ready for the Hero to return home, having completed his tasks. He concluded the story with Shrayth (who had found his 'balance') and their adopted daughters accompanying the Hero back to his Homeground. He felt that they were what he was taking back with him from his journey, and that they represented the combination of good and evil and the need for balance. Jeremiah felt that the Hero had learned how to love on this journey and concluded that '"things are not always what they seem", "anyone can be saved" and that "family love is the most important"'.
>
> I invited Jeremiah to put drawings and characters from the story into a timeline so that we could reflect back on all that had taken place on the Hero's Journey.

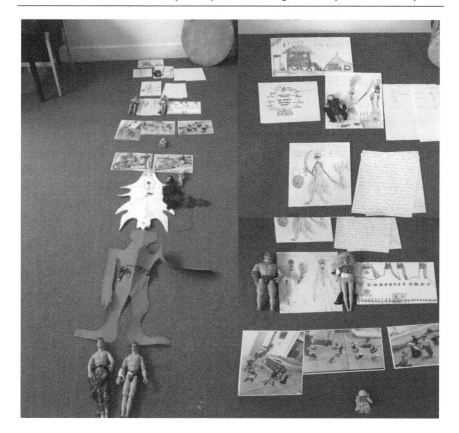

Figure 6.4 The timeline.

Reflections of Vignette 6

During 'check-in', he had spoken at length about an incident that had taken place on a school journey, when he had engaged in something that he had not really wanted to be part of. We discussed being able to say no in a situation where he did not want to do something. Jeremiah was very keen to know if I thought it was his fault or the fault of one of the others. He was able to relate the situation back to his experiences of the Hero's Journey and recognise that situations are often complicated. It made sense to Jeremiah in these terms.

Once he had looked back on the journey, Jeremiah began to consider what the next stage or 'episode' of the Hero's Journey would be.

> the Hero's Journey does not really end. It goes through a cycle, concluding itself with the call to the next cycle…and so it goes on.
>
> (Rebillot 1993, 181)

Jeremiah had begun to recognise that his journey is ongoing, and that as he grows and develops as a person, he will be constantly evolving and changing.

Interview with Jeremiah

Jeremiah and I continued weekly sessions after this work ended. During the coronavirus lockdown, we worked together online. In his first session during lockdown, Jeremiah explained that he had decided to support himself by creating another Hero's Journey. He had spent his first few weeks creating an in-depth story, following a process similar to our sessions. The following is a transcript of an interview held on zoom during lockdown in which Jeremiah describes in his own words the impact that the Hero's Journey process has had for him.

Question 1: How have you changed since first entering into the Hero's Journey?

> I feel like I'm not the little boy I was at the start. I used to be so naughty before, but I feel I can deal with stuff now. People used to pick on me, but there's not many people who bully me anymore. I use my stories to make myself happy and less lonely.

Question 2: What was the most important moment for you in your Hero's Journey?

> I see my characters like my children. I felt like Fulooko was a special character to me. It felt like I was in the story. He was a way to show my personality and how I was feeling.

Question 3: What does the Hero's Journey mean to you?

> I feel like it has shown me that no one is pure and no one is evil; they are all grey characters. I don't like how people present villains as all bad or Hero's as all good. People can be really nice and do horrible things at the same time.

Question 4: We had used the Hero's Journey in our therapy sessions together, why did you choose this way of working during lockdown?

> I found the Hero's Journey a way of dealing with stuff and also to have fun. I feel like I tell stories because stories help me grow. The Hero's Journey gets all of my feelings out. I like to put love, anger and passion in my stories. When I write down every character, every name, every word, it feels like I am part of the story, and you keep thinking about how these people feel, and it makes you feel like you are living in the moment in the story.

Question 5: What have you learned about yourself from the Hero's Journey?

I've seen a creative, special person who wants to change the world and wants to make things better. I want to show people that there is no such thing as just good or just evil. We are all entitled to our own story and get to choose who we become.

Conclusion

This chapter demonstrates the effectiveness of working at a deep level with clients with learning disabilities. The exploration of challenging feelings through the use of character and role can support the development of Theory of Mind and allow for the analysis of difficult and archetypal relationships in this client group. The Hero's Journey is a valuable tool for allowing clients with learning disabilities to be in control of their own process and to explore these complex feelings in a safe and contained way.

I believe that an important aspect of the dramatherapy process is working with the 'whole person' and allowing for the expression of difficult feelings that lie beyond the immediate learning disability. Those with learning disabilities have an equal right to be able to have the opportunity to process and explore the aspects of life that are challenging or traumatic. The Hero's Journey gave Jeremiah the space to manage his confusion and difficulties around his relationship with his father and the side of his family that he didn't know. It allowed for a safe and holding environment in which to make connections between the story and his real-life relationships and experiences. It gave him the space in which to reflect on how he felt. It is through being the leader of their own therapeutic process, and by expressing their 'voices', that those with learning disabilities can be supported to have agency in their own lives.

References

Baron-Cohen, S. 2008. *Autism and Asperger Syndrome.* New York: Oxford University Press.

Campbell, J. 2008. *The Hero with a Thousand Faces.* Novato California: New World Library.

Chesner, A. 1995. *Dramatherapy for People with Learning Disabilities – A World of Difference.* London and Philadelphia, PA: Jessica Kingsley Publishers.

Christensen, J. 2010. 'Making Space Inside – The Experience of Dramatherapy within a School-based Student Support Unit'. In: Karakou, V., ed. *Arts Therapies in Schools: Research and Practice*, 85–96. London and Philadelphia: Jessica Kingsley Publishers.

Johnson, D.R. 1994. 'The Dramatherapist 'in-role''. In: Jennings, S., ed. *Dramatherapy Theory and Practice 2*, 112–136 London and New York: Routledge.

Rebillot, R. 1993. *The Call to Adventure – Bringing the Hero's Journey to Daily Life.* San Francisco, CA: Harper Collins.

Watts, P. 1994. 'Therapy in Drama'. In Jennings, S., ed. *Dramatherapy Theory and Practice 2*, 44. London and New York: Routledge.

Chapter 7

Finding Sameer

A Client's Journey to Self-Discovery

Hayley Southern

Introduction

> We hope that dramatherapy will help Sameer to make meaningful conversations and connect with his emotions and the world around him.
>
> (College Staff)

This chapter explores how dramatherapy effectively supported a young person with severe learning disabilities, whose emotional development was hindered following a bereavement. It explores the two-and-a-half-year therapeutic process between a mixed-race dramatherapist and an Indian client, which took place at a college for students with special educational needs. Two interrelated but separate themes of the client's male gender identity and his emerging sexual identity will be explored, as well as his anger. How the challenges surrounding these themes can be safely explored within a therapeutic practice using dramatherapy techniques, and how dramatherapy can safely play the unplayable, will be discussed. This chapter highlights measures that were implemented to ensure ethical practice. The work was supported by robust supervision, details of which will not be presented here, as this chapter focuses on the therapeutic relationship.

Sameer was diagnosed with a language disorder and severe learning disabilities, which affected his ability to understand, respond, recall and relate. He had difficulty in group situations as he found it hard to process communication and focus his attention. At seven years old, Sameer's family experienced a trauma when his parents were involved in a car accident that resulted in the death of his mother. Sameer's father survived but suffered a critical brain injury and became unable to care for him. Sameer's two older sisters assumed parental responsibility, while continuing to care for their father.

Sameer was referred for individual dramatherapy by the college staff when he was sixteen years old. Nearly ten years had passed since the car accident and Sameer had reportedly never spoken about the loss of his parents, so there were concerns around his bereavement process. Although a sociable individual, who enjoyed the company of others, as well as knowing the difference between 'right and wrong', Sameer was extremely vulnerable and impressionable. He would

DOI: 10.4324/9781003091783-10

cooperate in anything that was asked of him and did not have the ability to 'stand-up for himself'.

College staff reported that Sameer was 'obsessed' with children's cartoons and had difficulty distinguishing between reality and fantasy. He often expressed himself using scripts and lines from movies or TV shows and had difficulty relating to the world around him. This was why they thought dramatherapy would be a helpful and accessible intervention.

Assessment

Sameer introduced himself with a formal handshake and was polite, friendly and enthusiastic about having dramatherapy – seemingly his habitual response to everything. He had developed particular life scripts to use in common interactions with people, which gave the impression that he did not have any learning disabilities. If conversations moved beyond these strategies, his engaged verbal communication seemed to become senseless and hard to understand. I found Sameer to be likeable, humorous and warm.

When meeting a client for the first time, I always ask 'what brings you here?' This open question lends itself to gaining valuable information, as well as providing the client an opportunity for reflection. Sameer did not know why he had been referred, other than having been informed that he was having dramatherapy. He was unaware of what dramatherapy entailed but was eager to attend. I considered how often Sameer was 'told' what to do and wondered whether he had any sense of control, ability to make choices or had a voice in the decision-making processes of his life. He did, however, enjoy stories and drawing. After sharing this passion with me, Sameer embarked on creating a story using a six-piece story-making (6PSM) assessment tool (Lahad 1992). This helps to indicate an individual's coping style when under stress. At the same time, it creates a metaphor representing something prominent in their life.

This assessment identified Sameer's difficulties with accessing his imagination; displayed by his attempt to fit the entire storyline of *Finding Nemo* (2003) (a son and father's journey of finding each other after being separated) into the 6PSM structure. This creative tool challenged Sameer's learned communication scripts; he seemed unable to create his own story. There was a desperate need for him to re-call all the events in this film. To support Sameer, I abandoned the offered structure and invited him to share the story, where he verbally recounted the entire plot in great detail. He used very little expression unless mimicking quotes from the film.

Finding a Story

The exploration of metaphors and stories is a useful resource within dramatherapy. The structure and containment of a story provides an aesthetic distance between client and subject matter, thus enabling them to unconsciously project a part of themselves and creatively play out what is discovered (Jones 2007). Stories facilitate an arena to safely encounter repressed material that can then be explored, forming a foundation for healing. This can help to instigate a change within clients, as well as create room for reflection, whereby the client can gain perspective on their difficulties (Mann Shaw 1996).

I was struck by the similarities between the film's storyline and Sameer's lived experience: it was as though this film captured many of the traumatic and signifi-cant events in his life. For instance, both Nemo and Sameer had a disability, their respective mothers had died, and both were overprotected by remaining family members. Although still living with his father, there was a dramatic change in their relationship where the father was no longer available due to the lasting effects of his brain injury. There was both a cognitive and relational separation. I wondered whether Sameer's fixation with this film served as a means of making sense of the changes in his life, and I was reminded how stories can be '…a magic mirror which reflects some aspects of our inner world…' (Bettelheim 1991, 309).

Initial Sessions

Using *Finding Nemo* (2003) as a metaphor for his bereavement, Sameer was sup-ported with exploring the loss of his parents and feeling alone. Sameer was invited to create a four-line script (Guarnieri 2017) based on this story, and he was so en-gaged that he created a six-line script titled 'Nemo and turtle work together to find Nemo's dad'. The script captured Nemo seeking help to find his father and formed a platform for Sameer to engage in role-play, which he was highly enthusiastic about. This exercise was the beginning of supporting Sameer to develop improvisa-tion skills, where he was enabled to continue the conversation and action beyond the lines: thus working away from his prescribed everyday scripts.

As the therapeutic relationship developed, Sameer became more confident in his interactions and expressed different emotions through these explorations. In Sameer's improvisations, Nemo's father was never found, and there was always a feeling that he would leave again if he ever was located. There was also a sense of the supportive character abandoning Nemo in the search for his father. Sameer became stuck, sad and frustrated during these moments. He continued to enact these Nemo-themed creative journeys for three months, which became very repetitive. This repe-tition of explorations within the dramatherapy sessions became an ongoing dynamic, which actually assisted and supported Sameer with processing his loss. Repeated behaviours are not uncommon for people with learning disabilities (Booker 2011).

Exploring Emotions

Sameer experienced great difficulty reflecting on his thoughts and emotions. He fre-quently identified as feeling 'happy' but was unable to verbally express why he felt this way and tended to describe unrelated events instead. He engaged well with cre-ative exercises, particularly using musical instruments, games and semi-improvised role-play, where he would express a variety of emotions. However, Sameer would reject feeling any emotions that he perceived as being negative, such as sadness or anger. With the aid of emotion cards, Sameer was able to name different emotions that were pictured but never associated himself with experiencing 'negative' emotions. With support, Sameer later began to represent feelings he did experience, such as 'happy', by using different colours and assigning them to areas on a body map. His favourite colour, blue, was 'happy' which he felt in his face when he smiled. Sameer struggled with continuing this exercise, until another student interrupted his session. Sameer became angry with this student and stated: 'I'll handle this, Hayley' in an assertive manner. He was protective of both his session and of me. This was a transitional moment four months into the dramatherapy process.

Sameer initially stated that he was still 'happy' until I drew attention to him clenching his hands, as well as breathing heavily, and physically mirrored this for him to see. Upon realising that I was not being judgemental, Sameer stated that he was feeling 'fierce' and was able to give other examples of when he had felt this way. This breakthrough enabled Sameer to continue to name, acknowledge and explore emotions by associating them with his lived experiences. He began to discuss the death of his mother in great detail. Sameer described a traditional Hindu practice, as he recalled seeing his mother in her casket at home and then 'sitting on the stairs as two gentlemen took her away to go to heaven'. He stated that he was 'broken-hearted' and appeared to speak off-script:

My heart was beating, then it burst. It went black and died. It is now black and dead. I have no heart.

Sameer spoke in a direct and detached manner, stating that he felt sad talking about this, while not showing any outward signs of sadness. This was the first time since the accident that he had spoken about it, and I found myself feeling a wave of emotion as he shared this with me. I felt my voice crack as I responded to him and recognised a sense of deeper connection and relationship between us – a countertransference. Freud identified transference as clients transferring attributes from significant relationships to therapists, with countertransference being the feelings therapists have in response to client transference (Rowan and Jacobs 2002). In this moment, I was aware of a maternal instinct arising within me and wanted to protect and comfort Sameer. I wondered whether Sameer unconsciously, in his transference, sought me as a mother. Furthermore, I questioned whether the wave of emotion I felt was the projection of the feelings Sameer could not hold. We went on to continue colouring the body map, where Sameer was able to acknowledge the tragedy of his broken and blackened heart.

Sameer continued to be open towards exploring emotions but was resistant to returning to his black heart or anything relating to 'sad', because he did not want to feel that way. He was motivated to explore his anger and wanted to be 'more fierce'. Being 'fierce' was directly linked to his wanting to be more assertive, to voice his own needs and 'stand-up' for himself, as described in his referral. Sameer explored this 'fierceness' through role-play as cowboys.

Semi-Structured Improvisations:
Processing Grief and Rage

Using role-play as a means of exploration helps enable clients to safely explore parts of themselves that they cannot recognise or comfortably express in society, it '…can serve as a crucial link among drama, everyday life, and therapy' (Landy 1993, 8). Sameer and I would discuss and outline a plan of what would transpire before enacting. Using role-play, Sameer explored themes of right and wrong, a sense of justice and his parents' car accident. As these stories progressed, Sameer allowed himself to express rage through cowboy-themed scenarios and began to share with me dark fantasies of torture.

Sameer created structured scenarios, where we took turns and role-reversed the roles of protagonist: 'sheriff' and antagonist: 'baddy'. During this, Sameer wanted the sheriff to have access to handcuffs to 'arrest the baddy'. This request was repeated over many sessions. Suggestions to represent handcuffs imaginatively were always declined, and Sameer found it difficult to move past this. I questioned the significance of these handcuffs and reflected on whether it would be safe to use them in the sessions. There are several connotations with handcuffs, and it felt taboo for a person of his age. I discussed this with college staff, who felt Sameer's gentle nature made him 'low risk' for the use of such props. Conversations with his family revealed his love of cowboy-themed films and a potential wish to re-enact what he had watched. I discussed in supervision Sameer's 'stuckness' in not moving past the desire to use handcuffs, as well as the use of props in the session, and what boundaries needed to be in place to keep both Sameer and myself safe.

In the event, for safety reasons, the handcuffs we used were self-releasing plastic toys that could easily be broken. Sameer and I made an agreement at the beginning of each session about how these would be used and how to signal that we needed to stop an exercise. This signal was rehearsed and was a safety measure that could be implemented by either party. This safety measure was applied to all role-play explorations within this intervention. With Sameer's difficulties with fantasy and reality in mind, importance was also placed on de-roling and giving sufficient time for reflection.

The handcuffs appeared to represent a sense of control and authority for Sameer as the sheriff, leaving me powerless and vulnerable in the role of the baddy. Sameer repeatedly directed me to enact being handcuffed, locked away, tortured, shot and dying and then brought back to life. Sameer's sheriff would use this opportunity to shout and rant, thus expressing his 'fierceness'.

Sameer also began to introduce car-related themes that were seemingly out of place. For example, a 'STOP' sign which the baddy overshot on his horse. This was closely related to the narrative of his parents' car accident. More aspects of this accident began to emerge. I speculated whether the dynamic between the sheriff and baddy was representational of his feelings towards his father.

Like his Nemo journey, Sameer continued these cowboy explorations for a prolonged period of time, where the events were always the same. Eventually, Sameer introduced a change that symbolised his being ready to move on, when he stated, 'the handcuffs are broken'. The handcuffs had been central to the sessions for eight months but were never mentioned again. They seemed to have served their purpose: providing security and containment for Sameer to safely explore and express difficult and dark feelings. Furthermore, the containment appeared to have nurtured Sameer's ability to become more assertive. He began to safely apply the skills he had developed within dramatherapy to his real life. Staff and family observed a change in Sameer's expression, communication and interaction: he 'stood-up' for himself by telling a peer in an appropriate context to 'Shut up, please'; Sameer's sisters noticed him 'snapping' at their father and call him 'annoying'.

Sexual Awakening and Gender Roles: Becoming a Man

A year into this intervention, Sameer continued to deepen his use of imagination and spontaneity through role-play and began to explore his identity and sense of worth. He repeatedly played a hero who defeated a dragon and saved the princess, which helped to develop his confidence, self-esteem and assertiveness. These dramatic explorations moved on with the metaphor of the princess becoming the prize and then developed into Sameer portraying a fantasy of the princess.

Sameer began to introduce aspects of his culture into his stories. Having a dual Hindu and Muslim heritage seemed to present Sameer with a level of confusion and a fantasy of adult life. It was unclear where this interpretation of his culture had stemmed from. However, dramatic explorations of the princess waiting on him and having all of his needs attended to, developed into enacting having multiple 'Hindu-Muslim' wives who adored and unconditionally loved him.

Sameer experienced difficulty with exploring or even considering other perspectives when expressing his strict notion of gender roles. During these moments, I struggled with my countertransference, because I felt enraged. His role at this point had a dominance which I found uncomfortable. Although I initially accepted this development and responded as a maidservant, there was a gender inequality, and I was concerned that I would be doing him a disservice if I was compliant and colluded with him. I also questioned whether Sameer was projecting onto my ethnicity, where my being half-Asian (with a similar complexion to him) might potentially fit Sameer's wish for a 'Hindu-Muslim' partner.

It was at this point that something else entered the relationship: there was an erotic undertone towards me in Sameer's transference. Sameer's therapeutic process could be likened to Freud's Oedipus Complex: where the child unconsciously becomes sexually attracted to their mother and views the father as their opponent, which can entail their becoming hostile towards them (Crain 2010).

In my countertransference, I started to feel differently towards Sameer. The roles he now chose had a sexual and misogynistic tone in their exploration, which conflicted with my personal feminist outlook. I viewed Sameer's latest character as an arrogant young man being confident of his sexual attraction and ability to attract all women. Within a year, Sameer's characters had developed from innocent and childlike, to angry, heroic, to now being misogynistic and sexual.

Through the improvised play, with me adopting the role as a feminine, fragile princess, Sameer explored a shift in the power dynamic. The relationship had left the realms of story and metaphor and had made its way into a new connection in the therapeutic space. Through Sameer's dominance within the improvised stories around cowboys, he was claiming an energy which had not been previously available to him. He was making a new connection to himself and to me as his drama-therapist. We had moved from the imaginary tales of Nemo, which had enabled the telling of his loss and bereavement, into the present relationship. The boy had become a man.

In response to my thought process, I began to challenge Sameer in my role, by voicing my opinions when being commanded and by objecting to some of his re-quests, which resulted in Sameer (in character) suddenly and passionately yelling that my character was to be 'stripped naked, tied to a pole and beaten in public' for not 'honouring the husband'. Both Sameer and I were taken aback by this statement. Sameer automatically came out of role (implementing our agreed signal) and quickly explained that it had been 'fantasy', a word he used meaning pretend. This demon-strated that he had developed his ability to distinguish between reality and fantasy.

This behaviour was in direct contrast to the polite and well-mannered handshak-ing Sameer that greeted me at the beginning of the intervention. I was concerned by the potency of this new layer to his rage and what it represented in the fam-ily context. I wondered whether this related to the loss of his mother, was being modelled at home or marked a breakaway from his sisters, who were protective of him. I was reminded of a similarity to his original story, where Nemo's growth as an individual was initially suffocated by the overprotection of love. The drama-therapy process had enabled a meeting with the hidden aspects of Sameer, what Jung would call the 'shadow'. This archetype incorporates the repressed and un-conscious primal parts of one's self (Jung 1990), and Sameer now felt safe enough for his shadow to be present in the sessions.

Our sessions moved away from role-play, partly because it had felt unsafe and hard to contain, given the clashing cultures, objectification and difficulty in gender role-reversal. With his protective siblings in mind, the sessions now focused on ex-ploring his family relationships. Sameer engaged well with this, and spoke fondly of each family member that he represented through drawing. However, there was a marked absence of his father. Sameer cried when I acknowledged this. He shared how he 'love[d]' his father 'very much' and was unable to reflect on this further. During this conversation, Sameer tried to stop himself from crying, and it was ap-parent to me that this was directly related to him being male and believing that: 'Men don't cry, I mustn't cry. I have to be strong'. We were now moving into an-other stage of the therapy, working directly with Sameer's own narrative.

After this, Sameer avoided talking about his family and wanted to return to role-play. He introduced this by beginning to talk about stories, which centred around him going to the park and bumping into me, where 'Hayley' brought a picnic, which they shared. Sameer was unable to elaborate on this further. He had appeared to regress to his former scripts, which were hard to understand and were interspersed with giggling. When using imaginative material through role-play, Sameer had been enabled to be free and spontaneous. However, working directly with his life story had prompted the return of his communication difficulties, and his energy was extremely high and unfocused. The scenario was suggestive of a romantic date.

Sessions later, Sameer appeared to be distracted by looking at my breasts. I was aware that this was natural for a developing adolescent and that Sameer was playing out a sexual attraction. I was not confident in working with this with Sameer and tried wearing different tops as a form of self-protection: I did not want to shame him, nor shame myself in my own discomfort. In the meantime, the imaginary date-like scenarios that Sameer continued to develop progressed to him pretending to take me for a meal at Nando's.

Adolescents with learning disabilities often present with a lower emotional developmental level of understanding, but physically, they experience puberty in line with their neuro-typical peers. There is a polarity between their physical, cognitive and emotional development. Although Sameer had significant learning disabilities, his sexual interest was a demonstration of a healthy physical development, the exploration of which was appropriate and in keeping with his being an adolescent. There was an innocence to this natural physical development; however, I had concerns regarding the vulnerability that Sameer's learning disabilities placed on him. He did not understand the physical changes and sexual urges he was experiencing, nor how to act on them, and could be easily taken advantage of. In Erikson's stages of growth, Sameer had appeared to have entered the identity versus confusion stage (Crain 2010), and his learning disabilities were making a confusing period of development even more challenging.

There was a need for psycho-education on understanding sex and relationships. The dramatherapy sessions were becoming difficult as Sameer raised many questions about puberty and sex. I felt this needed addressing more directly, outside the therapy. Sameer's questioning prompted me to initiate and liaise with the team leaders, working with Sameer, to provide him and his cohort with education around this subject.

The dramatherapy sessions had supported Sameer with his learning disabilities and understanding his feelings. Different types of love and relationships were explored through images depicting couples, families, teachers and therapists. This was done at the same time as explaining the boundaries of the therapeutic relationship. Sameer became emotional when he came to understand that 'romantic love' with me was not available. He stated that he did not have 'romantic' intentions towards me, which I acknowledged. The following few sessions witnessed a decline and disengagement from Sameer, where he presented as disheartened, he continued to cry but could not verbalise, or seem to know, why. He then missed a session, which was out of character for him. I felt worried and concerned that he was hurting: it felt like an impossible situation.

After his missed session, Sameer came back with a renewed sense of energy and wanted to explore 'romantic love'. Using puppets, he was enabled to safely express his feelings of rejection as he presented a couple separating. Sameer named the female character 'Hayley' and stated that this was not me. He went on to enact a character physically beating up the now ex-girlfriend for 'breaking my heart', while I assumed the role of a witness: one who sees and validates the experience of another. In the role, Sameer effectively expressed how he had been hurt by 'Hayley' and did not understand why she did not 'love' him in return. Sameer soon moved on from this scene of separation and expressed a desire to find a new girlfriend. Sameer asked me to adopt this new role, which was also called 'Hayley' (but was not me) and wanted me to physically kiss the puppet representing the male counterpart and call him 'sweet and cute'. I encouraged Sameer to assume this role himself and he continued to engage, portraying the journey of the two puppets courting and finding love. The couple dined at Nando's and went to Paris for their honeymoon, where they spent the entire time in 'bed', 'kissing and being romantic'.

After this exploration, Sameer showed an awareness of knowing, as well as accepting, that 'romantic love' between us was not possible. However, he now shared how he would like to have a 'Hindu-Muslim girlfriend'. During this reflection, Sameer appeared to feel shame regarding experiencing sexual feelings, as though he felt that it was wrong but did not know why. After further exploration, in which I validated and normalised his feelings, Sameer appeared reassured. He later shared that his family did not want him to have a girlfriend, and that if he did, she would need to be 'Hindu-Muslim'. I wondered whether this amalgamated culture was a reflection of his sister's marriage, and whether Sameer had been given an unrealistic stipulation.

Dreams, Aspirations and a Positive Goodbye: Finding Sameer's Story

After two years of working together, there was an impression that Sameer was using these sessions as a rehearsal for experiences and changes that he wanted in his life. The recent dynamics could be considered as him using the dramatherapist as a rehearsal girlfriend. Sameer continued to use his dramatherapy sessions as a tryout space, where he could develop his sense of identity.

Sameer explored his insecurities about being 'a loser' while playing pool in the sessions. This led on to experimenting how he would like to be seen, through adopting personas (mainly influenced by characters from films) in his interactions with me. Sameer wanted to be a man and continued to have a strict idea of gender roles, though this began to ease during our interactions. He also started to identify qualities in himself that he liked. As the sessions progressed, Sameer started to experiment with his appearance, such as his clothes and facial hair. He began to wear men's cologne and took pride in looking and feeling 'cool'.

During the six months before his leaving the college, and the ending of this intervention, Sameer began to look towards his future. His dreams of finding 'romantic love' continued, alongside plans to access further education in a specialist unit at a mainstream college. He also wanted to have a job and took pleasure in volunteering at a café under strict supervision. The college also supported Sameer in gaining further independence by providing travel training. Sameer appeared to flourish during this time and was enthusiastic about his future. However, he was resistant to exploring the ending of dramatherapy, stating that this was 'good' and that 'you will cry' when he left. I was aware that I would miss him and was worried about his vulnerability. Although Sameer had gained a sense of independence, and was developing important life skills, I felt protective of him. I felt like Marlin (Nemo's father), fearing that the world was not safe enough for Sameer and that he would be harmed in some way.

Sameer started to reject me; sharing his plans of having a leaving party to which everyone except me was invited. He drew a picture of me crying and being excluded from the fun. When reflecting on this, Sameer returned to his need for me to miss him; however, there was an element of self-protection, as Sameer would not cry or miss me in return.

Sameer experienced great difficulty during our last session together. He continued to reject me and resisted interactions to reflect on our journey over the past two and a half years. As the session drew to a close, I shared with Sameer how it had been a privilege to have worked with him, and that I had learned much during this time. Sameer stated that this had not been mutual and that I had not 'taught' him anything and then left the room without a handshake: his usual method of opening and closing sessions. I was left with a sense of loss. Later that day, Sameer returned to find me in the therapy space. He looked at me with emotion and said: 'Thank you Hayley, you taught me so much'.

I was reminded of the story of Nemo once again where, similarly to Marlin, I recognised Sameer's strength and resilience. He was no longer the vulnerable adolescent that I initially met but had grown into a young man.

Conclusion

Through client-led exploration of a storyline that mirrored his life experiences, Sameer was supported to face and express the grief of his loss and integrate this. Improvisational play that moved away from his habitual scripts facilitated dark fantasies to be witnessed and accepted. The increase in expression and spontaneity allowed Sameer to begin to identify new ways of interacting, to develop a sense of autonomy and to voice his wants and needs. The use of puppetry helped explore age-appropriate eroticism and learn about boundaries through using a distanced approach.

Effective communication with professionals involved in the care of people with learning disabilities is essential because of the vulnerability of this client group, who often struggle with the complexities of everyday life. The dramatherapist plays a crucial role in representing the client, while a multidisciplinary team approach helps ensure that the client is supported to develop to their full potential.

Fundamental to the work with Sameer was the link to staff in the college team. Sex education was introduced into the curriculum through my work with Sameer, which further supported his development.

This chapter demonstrates how dramatherapy holds the potential for growth and change. The intervention captures how Sameer's journey into adulthood was supported by boundaries, acceptance and creativity, where he shifted from a passive and childlike persona to being assertive and able to safely express and explore his individuality.

References

Bettelheim, B. 1991. *The Uses of Enchantment: The Meaning and Importance of Fairy Tales*. London: Penguin Books.

Booker, M. 2011. *Developmental Drama: Dramatherapy Approached for People with Profound or Severe Multiple Disabilities, Including Sensory Impairment*. London: Jessica Kingsley Publishers.

Crain, W. 2010. *Theories of Development: Concepts and Applications*. Essex: Pearson Education Limited.

Finding Nemo. 2003. Directed by Andrew Stanton and Lee Unkrich [Feature film]. Emeryville, CA: Walt Disney Pictures; Pixar Animation Studios.

Guarnieri, M. 2017. *Four-Line Script: A Dramatherapy Exercise*. Unpublished manuscript.

Jones, P. 2007. *Drama as Therapy: Theory, Practice and Research*. London: Routledge.

Jung, C.G. 1990. *The Archetypes and the Collective Unconscious*, 2nd Edition. Oxon: Routledge.

Lahad, M. 1992. 'Storymaking: An Assessment Method of Coping with Stress: Six-piece Storymaking and BASIC Ph'. In: Jennings, S., ed. *Dramatherapy: Theory and Practice 2*, 150–163. London: Routledge.

Landy, R.J. 1993. *Persona and Performance: The Meaning of Role in Drama, Therapy, and Everyday Life*. London: Jessica Kingsley Publishers.

Mann Shaw, S. 1996. 'Metaphor, Symbol and the Healing Process in Dramatherapy'. In: *Dramatherapy*. Volume 18, Issue 2, 2–5. London: Sage.

Rowan, J. & Jacobs, M. 2002. *The Therapist's Use of Self*. Maidenhead: Open University Press.

Chapter 8

"We are lots of things"

Exploring Dramatic Imitation with Adolescents in Special Education

Amanda Musicka-Williams

Prologue: Dramatherapy in Australia

It may seem that dramatherapy is in its infancy in Australia. In many professional contexts, it is a relatively unknown practice. However, there are dramatherapists across the country, and many have practised here for some time. Professional networks for creative arts therapists are currently expanding, providing increased opportunity for professional dialogue and promotion of the practice. Many of the dramatherapists currently practising in Australia trained overseas. However, dramatherapy training at a diploma or postgraduate level has also been offered in Western Australia, New South Wales and Queensland. While a number of training institutes currently offer courses in a mixed modality approach to creative arts therapy, from 2020, the University of Melbourne has offered master's-level creative arts therapy training, which specialises in either dramatherapy or dance movement therapy. On completion, trainees are eligible for professional registration with AN-ZACATA, the Australia, New Zealand and Asia professional association for creative arts therapists. In addition, the Creative Arts and Music Therapies Research Unit at the University of Melbourne conducts research in creative arts therapies both nationally and internationally.

Those who have worked as dramatherapists in Australia have had to work hard to gain professional recognition in diverse contexts including: education, community and private mental health, disability support services, domestic violence support services, care for the elderly, medical and forensic settings. As a collective of established and emerging Australian dramatherapists, we are optimistic, encouraged by the growth in professional interest and training, that dramatherapy will continue to expand here, to offer meaningful therapeutic practice to those who can benefit from a unique, dramatic approach to knowing, being and becoming more of oneself.

A note on terminology: In this chapter, the term "intellectual disability" is used instead of "learning disability." In Australia, a learning disability refers to difficulties with academic skills and information processing, and these challenges are generally addressed through specific teaching strategies. However, a person diagnosed with an intellectual disability is recognised as having an intellectual impairment resulting in lifelong challenges related to self-management and independent living skills.

DOI: 10.4324/9781003091783-11

Introduction

This chapter tells the story of a research journey. A journey undertaken by one practitioner researcher and 15 adolescent participants, who share in the telling of what was discovered along the way. This is the story of how we used dramatherapy as an accessible research tool, to enable adolescents diagnosed with intellectual and developmental disabilities to have an opportunity *"to tell people what we really think."* This is a simple tale, about how these young people wish *"to play with,"* *"learn from"* and *"join in with others."* A tale about how they identified a means through which they could achieve these aims. This is a story about *"copying"* and the therapeutic power of dramatic imitation.

Motivation for the research outlined in this chapter grew from long-term practice as a dramatherapist in special education. Relationships forged from that experience privileged me with opportunities to witness the capacity for insight that exists among the young people there. Undertaking this research provided me with the opportunity to challenge a prevailing assumption that people with intellectual disabilities have limited capacity to express personal insight (Blackman 2003; Sinason 2010). In telling our research story, I include the participants' own words. In sharing participants' unique perspectives on their relationships, how they learn from others and what serves to inform their sense of relational connectedness, I acknowledge them as the true experts of their own experiences (Knox et al. 2000).

The research explored adolescent participants' *"important relationships"* and experiences of interpersonal learning through group dramatherapy in special education. The participants chose to focus on *"important relationships"* in common recognition that relationships were *"the most important thing"* in their lives but also *"tricky,"* *"hard"* and *"confusing."* Using dramatic processes to explore these relationships enabled participants to reflect on how they experienced relational connection in ways that are meaningful to them. The participants reflected that their personal outcomes related to the dramatherapy experience were largely achieved through *"copying,"* a conscious imitation of others and real-life experiences.

In this chapter, I contextualise the sharing of our research findings by briefly outlining the approach to research, specific context and aims of our study. The rest of this chapter discusses our findings. Research vignettes are used to illustrate some of the dramatherapy processes that participants engaged with, as well as their responses to the central idea of *"copying others."* It presents a discussion grounded in participant insight of how dramatherapy might consciously utilise a specific kind of *"copying"* in the form of dramatic imitation, to better enable adolescents with intellectual and developmental disabilities to access an extended experience of themselves and enhanced sense of relational connection to others.

Approach to Research

The research was undertaken in a place of long-term clinical practice. It was therefore viewed as practitioner research; an approach to research frequently conducted within the creative arts therapies (Jones 2010; Miller 2014, 2017). The general aim of practitioner research is to undertake research, which addresses the needs of participants in relation to a specific clinical context. Outcomes serve to inform future practice in similar contexts, with similar participants (Yanos & Ziedonis 2006).

Methodological Choices

Constructivist grounded theory was chosen as an approach to research which enabled the participants' voices and experiences to be centralised in theory generation (Charmaz 2011, 2014). Research data was viewed as a mutual creation between researcher and research participants, promoting a position of mutuality within the research process (Charmaz & Mitchell, 1996). This aligned with an overall intention to enable participants to actively engage and represent their experiences in creative ways, which were authentic and meaningful to them (Snow & D'amico 2009). The research design was further influenced by "inclusive research" (Walmsley & Johnson 2003) and "arts informed research" (Leavy 2015; McNiff 2007). Both approaches offered ways of constructing and reflecting on knowledge that weren't overly reliant on spontaneous intellectualisation and verbal ability.

Context

The research was undertaken at Port Phillip Specialist School in Melbourne, Australia. The school supports the learning needs of students diagnosed with mild to severe intellectual disability, a variety of developmental delays and genetic conditions. A visual and performing arts curriculum is employed to achieve educational and living skill goals.

Participants

Fifteen adolescents aged 15–18 participated in the research. Thirteen were diagnosed with mild-moderate intellectual disability while two were described as having significant developmental delays, which meant they presented in ways which enabled their inclusion in special education. Many participants were diagnosed with other genetic conditions and/or impairments and presented with varying verbal ability.

Research Aims/Focus

Two broad interrelated aims informed the focus of the research inquiry:

– To explore and reflect upon participants' experiences and perceptions of the key relationships in their lives through group dramatherapy and creative interviewing, which embedded dramatic techniques into a semi-structured interview process to elicit and extend the participants' reflections.

– To reflect with participants on the idea of using dramatherapy as a tool for experiential or action-based learning (Bailey 2010, 2014; Butler 2017) in specific relation to the development of interpersonal skills.

The interrelated focus aimed to acknowledge the ways in which therapeutic goals are often intertwined with learning processes when dramatherapy occurs in an educational context (Frydman & Mayor 2019; Holmwood 2014). The data collected from participants supported the decision to maintain a dual focus of inquiry, as participants' reflections readily linked their dramatherapy experiences to personal learning outcomes.

The Central Research Phenomenon: "We copy"

Analysis of the research data, which consisted of 28 semi-structured creative interviews, resulted in the discovery of a central phenomenon at play within the participants' experience of group dramatherapy. This discovery is summarised by two words commonly expressed by participants: *"We copy."* Understanding the phenomenon of *"copying"* was pivotal to understanding participants' experience of the group dramatherapy process. Furthermore, it provided insight into how the participants established and expressed relational connection, and how they learn from others in ways which enabled extended self-presentations and capabilities to be performed. Invited to explore their idea of *"copying others"* within both group dramatherapy and individual interviews, participants expressed and enacted conscious reasons for this tendency to imitate.

> Copying? Yeah we do that, we do it a lot… We do it because we're teenagers… Everybody does it… but some people do it more… I copy to remember people it makes me happy… I copy to learn… do something different… I copy to be included… to not be lonely… I copy 'cos it's the easiest way to know what to do… to follow along with the others… I copy when I can't be bothered. Because it's easier to let someone else come up with the ideas… I copy to be normal… To show that I can do what other people can… I copy to play… It's a way of talking and being with my friends… I copy cos it's fun… I copy to try something new…
> (Musicka-Williams 2020a)

Participants acknowledged strengths and weaknesses with "copying others" describing it as "good and bad," and explaining, "It depends on who's doing it and how they go about it." "There's a right and a wrong way to copy." Participants reflected "copying others" the right way, enabled play, learning, connection and a demonstration of one's extended capabilities.

> When we copy others, we show that we can do what the other kids can do it just takes us a little longer is all.
> (Theodora)

However, one could easily get it wrong and then the copying received an unfavour-able response.

> Well, it makes me think of copy cats and well that's just annoying... Like it can't be everything... You can start with copying but eventually you have to find a way to somehow make it your own, do your own thing.
>
> (Theodora)

Describing the presence of copying in dramatherapy participants explained:

> In dramatherapy it is easy to join in because you just watch what the others are doing and then you copy.
>
> (Ace)

> In dramatherapy there is lots of copying. It's both similar and different to the copying we do elsewhere.
>
> (Hyber)

Participant reflections acknowledged how the use of dramatic imitation in drama-therapy provides them with a tool through which *"[they] copy and act out things from real life."* Copying others or aspects of real life was seen as key to engaging with the dramatic space and connecting with group members in ways which ena-bled imaginal possibilities to be co-created and explored. Participants recognised that while dramatic imitation provided them with an accessible and embodied entry point into the play space, it offered something beyond the limitations of *"straight copying."* The dramatic imitation was different too because it involved a creative extension of self. The opportunity to explore not only what is but what could be or what one could be.

> In dramatherapy we act things out...You can try something new, be something different. Because I am lots of different things, everyone is.
>
> (Aimee)

A Co-Created Grounded Theory on "copying" in Group Dramatherapy

Findings from our research were presented through co-construction of a final grounded theory. This theory explained how copying is central to enabling participants access to therapeutic change. Participants consciously copied others, both within-group dramatherapy and wider social contexts for the purposes of *"playing with," "learn-ing from"* and *"joining in with"* or feeling connected to others. Figure 8.1 provides a visual summation of the grounded theory and the interrelating functional properties/purposes of *"copying others."* The grounded theory was constructed as a simple, ac-cessible visual, so participants could identify and reflect upon their collective ideas.

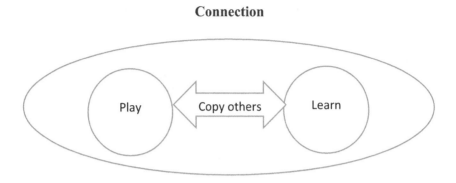

Figure 8.1 Accessible representation of the co-constructed grounded theory.

Dramatic imitation was viewed as a kind of *"copying"* employed in drama-therapy, where participants got to *"copy each other and stuff from real life."* In doing so, participants found access to play, learning and connecting as their self-identified therapeutic objectives (Musicka-Williams 2020a). From a therapist's perspective and supported by the views of the participants who acknowledge that *"copying is ok, but it can't be everything"; "eventually you have to find a way to make it your own" "and try something new, be something different,"* the overall goal is to move participants from a tendency towards imitative fidelity to an experience of imitative flexibility (Legare & Neilson 2015). In pursuing this goal, the group dramatherapy process may be viewed as an imitative learning experience.

Key Theoretical Concepts

Imitative learning: Imitative learning is a social learning practice (Over & Carpenter 2012) where a learner acquires new behaviours or skills through imitating others (Cale Kruger 2011; Metzolf 2011). Participants referred to this as *"watching and copying so you know what to do"* or *"seeing and doing."* They explained, *"copying others is the easiest way to learn."*

High-fidelity imitation: High-fidelity imitation occurs when the learner completes a direct replication of specific skill sets modelled by another through action sequences (Legare et al. 2015; Legare & Neilson 2015). Participants referred to this as, *"straight copying."*

Over imitation: Over imitation occurs when a learner imitates all detailed actions regardless of whether they are purposeful in achieving an end goal (Legare & Neilson 2015). Participants referred to this as, *"being a copy-cat."*

Imitative flexibility: Imitative flexibility refers to a learner's capacity to demonstrate appropriate levels of innovation when imitating others (Legare et al. 2015; Legare & Neilson 2015). Participants referred to this process as, *"copying something and then finding a way to make it your own"* (Musicka-Williams 2020a, 2020b).

Playing with Dramatic Imitation

Drama is an imitative art-form (Chasen 2011, 2014; Jennings 2011; Rasmussen 2008; Whitehead 2001) which draws from real-life experience and the notion that every day we are invested in our real-life dramas (Landy 1993, 2009). Participants reflected on *"copying"* as a core feature of their experience of the dramatic process in group dramatherapy.

> In dramatherapy we copy each other. I like it when people copy me to play. Playing together is like copying and being copied. In dramatherapy we copy each other's stories. Copying words and actions.
>
> (Ava)

Many participants described play as their primary means of communication, particularly in peer relationships where dramatic copying of others was seen as a familiar form of play, *"it's a way of hanging out"* or *"mucking around together."*

> When I am with my friends, we copy each other. It makes me happy. We copy each other in dramatherapy too. I like it. It's fun.
>
> (Liz)

Copying as a Necessary Warm-up

Participants reflected that everything they created in dramatherapy grew from an initial act of imitation. *"Copying others or real life"* was viewed as a necessary warm-up phase. Playful copying of others' words or actions alleviated the pressure associated with a need to be spontaneous. Embodied imitation provided an accessible and developmentally appropriate bridge into creative innovation, at an adolescent stage of life where copying peers is expected. *"We do it because we are teenagers." "Teenagers copy each other a lot."* Dramatic copying of others provided space for necessary repetition and extended processing. Utilising participants' conscious copying of others in dramatherapy served to illustrate how habitual tendencies could be harnessed as creative strengths, while recognising how all human creativity is constructed by innovating on what has already been conceived. *"We all copy. Some of us just do it more than others."* Incorporating structured dramatic tasks built upon a foundation of playful copying enabled participants for whom spontaneous acts were challenging to direct and pace their own therapeutic experience.

Imitation as a Playful Approach to Learning

For the participants, "*copying is the easiest way to learn,*" because it enables imitative learning, a pathway to personal learning outcomes which is enhanced for participants in special education through a playful dramatic approach. Capitalising on imitation as a basic form of dramatic expression (Chasen 2011, 2014; Jennings 2011; Rasmussen 2008), the participants view the dramatherapy space as a place of accessible learning.

> In dramatherapy we are playing. We play to learn. We are learning about relationships and stuff. It's a fun way to learn. Learning about ourselves and others, learning how to act, how to behave, how to be.
>
> (Hyber)

This participant's linking of the group dramatherapy to personal learning outcomes highlights the potential for dramatherapy to be viewed as an experiential and imitative learning process.

VIGNETTE 1   Understanding Others

Luke described difficulty with spontaneous thinking and conversations:

> "It's hard for me to answer. The thoughts get stuck. It happens a lot. I don't know why, they just do." However, he also reflected, "It's different in dramatherapy I have lots of ideas there. Dramatherapy is easier because I watch and follow the others and then I have ideas of my own."

When asked to reflect on a group exercise, Luke often responded, "*I don't really know.*" However, when invited to dramatically imitate what he witnessed, he was able to describe what the others had been doing, as well as how he thought they might be feeling. He explained:

> When I copy, I begin to understand what might be going on with the other person, how they might be feeling.

Participants readily linked embodied dramatic imitation to their enhanced ability to understand and empathise with the experiences of others (Pitruzzella 2017). Reflecting on active witnessing as a core therapeutic process in dramatherapy (Jones 1996, 2007, 2016), dramatic imitation of peers appeared to offer Luke an extended and embodied experience of this witnessing process. The physical act of copying peers enabled Luke to tap into his own capacity for embodied knowledge of another and subsequently articulate a felt sense of empathy (Koch & Fuchs 2011).

VIGNETTE 2   Becoming an Adult

Many participants in their final year of school explored adulthood within their dramatic enactments. Becoming an adult was a role of which they expressed feeling both excitement and trepidation. Adults could *"do more grown-up stuff," "do what they want"* and *"don't have to go to school anymore."* However, they also had *"more responsibilities"* and participants expressed common concern about what life after school would offer.

Invited to explore the adult role, participants impersonated familiar adults as an entry point into developing a role of their own. During the interviews, Rory watched video footage of himself playing an adult. He explained that he chose the role because, *"I am usually silly and adults are serious...I wanted to do something different."* A self-confessed imitator, Rory explained, *"I copy other people all the time. I do it cos it's funny, it entertains people, makes others laugh."* However, in observing himself in the adult role, he noted, *"I am being really different."* A more direct imitation rather than what he described as a habitual tendency to *"mimic others as a way to tease"* resulted in a different self-presentation. Reflecting on this, he said, *"I am being really quiet and serious because that's what adults do. I copy the adults to know how to be one."*

Rory's reflections support a dramatic view of life, in which human behaviour is viewed as performative and constructed through imitative acts (Goffman 1956; Landy 1991, 1993). By *"copying"* others, participants acquired access to an extended role repertoire. Dramatic imitation became a tool to challenge preconceptions of self and the limited social roles offered to people with intellectual disability (Kittlesea 2014).

Needing to Belong

Participants' self-identified therapeutic objectives, *"to play with," "to learn from"* and *"join in"* with others, represent basic human needs. They pursued these experiences in order to access one of the most fundamental human needs of all, a sense of belonging (Baumeister & Leary 1995). Participants explained they enjoyed dramatherapy because there, *"Everyone is equal...and that doesn't usually happen." "We take turns leading and following. Everyone gets their turn and everyone is included."* In group dramatherapy, where imaginal, dramatic play provided a space where anything is possible (Sajnani 2016), belonging was attainable for young people who think that, *"We get left out because we are different."*

VIGNETTES 3 AND 4   Being Included

Kyle described difficulty forming and sustaining friendships at school. A reality which he described as being the result of both his peer's response to features of his disability, and his own expressions of anger about this, which pushed others away. Kyle perceived a pecking order among classmates which was then acted during group dramatherapy. He reflected on scenes exploring peer friendships where some participants were excluded within the drama:

> It shows what's really happening... Well in our class group there are insiders and outsiders.... It's kind of like there are kings and queens, and everyone has to follow and do what the king says.... And some get included and some of us get discluded.

He described making unsuccessful attempts to join in with peers by *"copying the others,"* after which he said, *"I act out because I get angry... it makes things worse."* Asked about his experience of these same peers during dramatherapy, he said,

> I just want everyone to be treated equally. Sometimes that happens in dramatherapy. Everyone gets to have their turn. Everyone gets to have their say and people have to listen. I wish this would happen more often. I just want everyone to be included.

Another participant, Hyber, similarly described, *"I get left out... I just want them to be my friends. Play with me. Include me."* She too cited "copying," as the solution and sought to include herself by imitating peers.

> Copying is good, because then other people are nice to me. I copy my classmates, what they do, how to listen, when to stop. Copying is easy it helps me... In dramatherapy we do lots of copying. Sometimes the others copy me. I wish that would happen more elsewhere.

Dramatic and playful copying of others in dramatherapy was seen to provide a successful extension of self which moved beyond habitual *"straight copying"* of others. It enabled some participants a new experience of relational connection and equality with peers, which ultimately enhanced a longed-for sense of belonging.

Towards Imitative Flexibility

Participants' reflections on their conscious copying of others provide insight into the social and imitative learning mechanisms utilised by adolescents diagnosed with intellectual or developmental disabilities. Their conscious recognition of the need to *"copy others and then somehow make it your own"* reflects a need to extend high-fidelity imitation (Legare et al. 2015; Legare & Neilson 2015) or *"straight copying"* into imitative flexibility (Legare et al. 2015; Legare & Neilson 2015) and the opportunity to *"try something new."* It is a combination of imitative practices which are employed in dramatherapy which enabled participants to *"show others what we can do"*, successfully engaging participants in social learning tasks, the acquisition of new skills and self-presentations. Dramatic imitation provided a familiar tool through which participants could enter the play space and explore their own capacity for imitative flexibility. Through dramatic *"copying"*, participants effectively extended their role repertoires (Landy 1991, 1993, 2009), explored imaginal possibilities and experienced the opportunity to direct change through role play, which served as a rehearsal space for real life (Weiner 2016). Through conscious engagement with dramatic imitation, participants were able to reflect on a growing ability to reconstruct a new reality out of pieces of the original life experience (Jones 2007).

> In dramatherapy we play, we act things out and you can try something new, be something different... I learnt in dramatherapy that I am lots of things, everybody is.
>
> (Amiee)

VIGNETTE 5 Breaking the Rules

Harry expressed equal, if slightly incongruent, love for the freedom of creative practice and a strict adherence to rules. Asked about his relationships, Harry described a code of conduct which included *"We don't touch... I only touch objects. I am not good at touching people, only objects."* The group explored intimacy within different types of relationships through dramatic enactment. This exploration began with a mirroring exercise in pairs. After some time mirroring his partner's actions, Harry spontaneously reached out to touch his partner and then continued the mirroring while holding his partner's hands. Upon witnessing the video recording of this moment, Harry appeared surprised. *"I am touching my friend. I'm smiling. I look happy."* I agreed, but reminded him he had told me he didn't touch anybody. *"Well, yes,"* he responded, *"The rules are different when you are playing."*

Harry's reflection on his own engagement with dramatherapy illustrates the overall therapeutic aim as presented in our co-constructed grounded theory, the ability to move participants from rigid attempts at high-fidelity imitation into a new experience of their own capacity for imitative flexibility. In the group dramatherapy process, Harry moved from someone who always adhered to strict rules, both those presented by others and those he self-imposed, to someone who spontaneously extended the play action. In doing so, Harry discovered a new experience of himself in relationship to others which he was able to transfer beyond the therapeutic space.

Conclusion

This chapter has outlined research which explored *"important relationships"* and interpersonal learning processes with adolescents in special education. *"Copying"* or imitating others and aspects of real-life experience was revealed as an accessible dramatic tool and core therapeutic process within the dramatherapy experience (Jones 1996, 2007, 2016). *"Copying"* enabled adolescents with intellectual and developmental disabilities to achieve their own self-defined therapeutic objectives: to play with, learn from and connect to others in ways which enhanced a sense of belonging. Consciously playing with dramatic imitation enabled participants to creatively extend upon these acts, to move from high-fidelity imitation towards a capacity for imitative flexibility (Legare et al. 2015; Legare & Neilson 2015). Participants described dramatherapy as providing a *"fun and easy way to learn about ourselves and other people."* Their insights give us opportunity to consider further the ways in which dramatherapy might be considered a therapeutic approach which can simultaneously address therapeutic and educational goals relevant to a special education setting, where there is a focus on developing life skills.

"We all copy." Imitation is a fundamental human behaviour and the basic building block of dramatic play (Jennings 2011; Whitehead 2001). If we acknowledge *"copying"* as an important therapeutic tool, if we consciously play with it and creatively extend upon it, we offer accessible pathways to experiential and imitative learning, expressions of youth culture, extended ways of being and relating for adolescents with intellectual and developmental disabilities. Through sharing our research story, I invite other dramatherapists to explore further the therapeutic effects of imitation and to consider how centralising participant insight within dramatherapy research and recommendations for future practice might assist us to further develop a practice which reflects the therapeutic experiences that participants desire to have.

Acknowledgements

Thank-you to the participants, without you I would have nothing to share. Thanks to Port Phillip Specialist School, the Victoria Education Department, The Creative Arts and Music Therapies Research Unit at Melbourne University and supervisors Professor Katrina McFerran, Professor Anna Seymour and Dr Lucy Bolger for guidance and encouragement.

References

Bailey, S. 2010. *Barrier-free theatre*. Enumclaw, Washington State: Idyll Arbor.
Bailey, S. 2014. 'Leveling the playing field in the classroom through embodied teaching and theatre.' *American Alliance for Theatre in Education's Washington State Theatre's in Our Schools Conference.* Seattle, WA (1–9.).

Baumeister, R.F. & Leary, M.R. 1995. 'The need to belong: Desire for interpersonal attachments as a fundamental human motivation.' In: *Pyschological Bulletin, 117*(3), 497–529. Worcester, MA: American Psychological Association.

Blackman, N. 2003. *Loss and learning disability.* Fort Worth, TX: Worth Publishing Ltd.

Butler, J.D. 2017. 'Re-examining Landy's four-part model of drama therapy education.' In: *Drama Therapy Review, 3*(1), 75–87. Albany, NY: Intellect.

Cale Kruger, A. 2011. 'Imitation, communion and culture.' In: Garrels, S.R., ed. *Mimesis and Science* (111–128). East Lansing: Michigan State University Press.

Charmaz, K. 2011. 'Grounded theory methods in social justice research.' In: Denzin, N.K., ed. *Strategies of Qualitative Inquiry* (291–336). London: SAGE.

Charmaz, K. 2014. *Constructing grounded theory.* 2nd edition. London: SAGE.

Charmaz, K. & Mitchell, R.G. 1996. 'The myth of silent authorship: Self, substance and authorship in ethnographic writing.' In: *Symbolic Interaction,* 19(4), 285–302. Wiley Online Library.

Chasen, L. 2014. *Engaging mirror neurons to inspire connection and social emotional development in children and teens on the autism spectrum.* London: Jessica Kingsley.

Chasen, L.R. 2011. *Social skills, emotional growth and drama therapy: Inspiring connection on the Autism spectrum.* London: Jessica Kingsley Publishers.

Frydman, J.S. & Mayor, C. 2019. 'Drama therapists in schools: Holding and exploring multiple paradigms.' In: *Drama Therapy Review, 5*(1): 3–6. Albany, NY: Intellect.

Goffman, E. 1956. *The presentation of self in everyday life.* New York: Anchor Books.

Holmwood, C. 2014. *Drama education and dramatherapy: Exploring the space between disciplines.* London: Routledge.

Jennings, S. 2011. *Healthy attachments and neuro-dramatic play.* London & Philadelphia: Jessica Kingsley Publisher.

Jones, P. 1996. *Drama as therapy, theatre as living.* London: Routledge.

Jones, P. 2007. *Drama as therapy volume 1.* London: Routledge.

Jones, P. 2010. *Drama as Therapy Volume 2.* London: Routledge.

Jones, P. 2016. 'How do dramatherapists understand client change?' In: Jennings, S. & Holmwood, C., eds. *Routledge International Handbook of Dramatherapy* (77–91). London & New York: Routledge.

Kittlesea, A. 2014. 'Self presentations and intellectual disability.' In: *Scandanavian Journal of Disability Research, 16*(1), 29–44. Taylor and Francis Online.

Knox, M., Mok, M. & Parmenter, T.R. 2000. 'Working with the experts: Collaborative research with people with an intellectual disability.' In: *Disability & Society, 15*(1), 49–62. Taylor and Francis Online.

Koch, S. & Fuchs, T. 2011. 'Embodied arts therapies.' In: *Arts in Psychotherapy, 38*(4), 276–280. Science Direct Online.

Landy, R.J. 1991. 'The dramatherapy role method.' In: *Journal of Dramatherapy, 14(2),* 7–15. London: Sage.

Landy, R.J. 1993. *Persona and performance: The meaning of role in drama, therapy and everyday life.* London: Jessica Kingsley Publishers.

Landy, R.J. 2009. 'Role theory and the role method of dramatherapy.' In: Johnson, D.R., ed. *Current Approaches in Dramatherapy* (2nd edition: 7–27). Springfield, IL: Charles C. Thomas Publishers.

Leavy, P. 2015. *Method meets art: Arts based research.* New York: Guilford Publications.

Legare, C.H. & Neilson, M. 2015. 'Imitation and innovation: The dual engines of cultural learning.' In: *Trends in Cognitive Sciences, 19*(11), 688–699. Neurodiem Online.

Legare, C.H., Wen, N.H., Hermann, P.A. & Whitehouse, H. 2015. 'Imitative flexibility and the development of cultural learning.' *Cognition, 142*, 351–361. Science Direct Online.

McNiff, S. 2007. 'Arts-based research.' In: Knowles, J.G. & Cole, A.L., eds. *Handbook of the Arts in Qualitative Research* (29–40). London: SAGE.

Metzolf, A.N. 2011. 'Out of the mouths of babes: Imitation, gaze, and intentions in infant research – the 'like me' framework.' In: Garrels, S.R., ed. *Mimesis and Science* (55–74). East Lansing: Michigan State University Press.

Miller, C. 2014. 'Introduction.' In: Miller, C., ed. *Assessment and Outcomes in the Arts Therapies* (11–14). London: Jessica Kingsley Publisher.

Miller, C. 2017. 'Practice-based evidence: Therapist as researcher, using outcome measures.' In: *Dramatherapy, 38*(1), 4–15. London: Routledge.

Musicka-Williams, A. 2020a. *No innovation without imitation: Using dramatherapy to explore relationships and interpersonal learning processes with adolescents in special education.* Minerva-access.unimelb.edu.au. Http://hdl.net/11343/258585

Musicka-Williams, A. 2020b. '"We copy to join in, to not be lonely": Adolescents in special education reflect on using dramatic imitation in group dramatherapy to enhance relational connection and belonging.' In: *Frontiers in Psychology, 11*, 3069. Online: Frontiers in Psychology.

Over, H. & Carpenter, M. 2012. 'Imitative learning in humans and animals.' In: Seel, N.M., ed. *Encyclopedia of the Sciences of Learning* (87). New York: Springer.

Pitruzzella, S. 2017. *Drama, creativity and intersubjectivity.* London: Routledge.

Rasmussen, B. 2008. 'Beyond imitation and representation: Extended comprehension of mimesis in drama education.' In: *Research in Drama Education: The Journal of Applied Theatre and Performance, 13*(3), 307–319. Taylor and Francis Online.

Sajnani, N. 2016. 'How acting 'as if' can make a difference.' In: *Drama Therapy Review, 2*(2), 163–166. Albany, NY: Intellect.

Sinason, V. 2010. *Mental handicap and the human condition.* London: Free Association Books.

Snow, S. & D'amico, M. eds. 2009. *Assessment in the creative arts therapies: Designing and adapting assessment tools for adults with developmental disabilities.* Springfield, IL: Charles C. Thomas Publisher.

Walmsley, J. & Johnson, K. 2003. *Inclusive research with people with learning disabilities: Past, present and future.* London: Jessica Kingsley Publishers.

Weiner, D.J. 2016. 'Removing personal constraints via proxy scene enactment.' In: *Drama Therapy Review, 2(*2), 183–193. Albany, NY, USA: Intellect.

Whitehead, C. 2001. 'Social mirrors and shared experiential worlds.' In: *Journal of conciousness studies, 8*, 12–32. Interaction Design Foundation Online.

Yanos, P.T. & Ziedonis, D.M. 2006. 'The patient-oriented clinician-researcher: Advantages and challenges of being a double agent.' In: *Open Forum, 57*(2), 249–253. Oxford Academic.

Part 3

On to Adulthood

Chapter 9

Yes I am, Here I Am

Using Confirmation as an Antidote to Cultural Shame

Melanie Beer and Gillian Downie

Tom

It was Tom's turn to open the box. He reached in to see what he would find this week. The other group members looked on with curiosity as he pulled out a wand. He pointed it at Mel stating, 'Abracadabra! You're a frog'. Mel immediately responded through movement, taking on the shape and sound of a Frog. Tom's face lit up and he laughed. He said, 'I've turned Mel into a frog!' Pointing the wand once again at Mel, she released the shape, resuming her position in the chair.

When Tom first started therapy, he was in his 50s, living with his parents. His decisions were made for him, and it was difficult for Tom to find a voice. He was referred to the arts therapies service because of the impending loss of his ageing parents, who have since died. Within the dramatherapy group, we have seen Tom gradually discover his autonomy and initiative. Responding to the invitation to 'take what he needed' from the box, he pulled out an imaginary wand, trying out his power. Mel embodied the impact of his action. Her dynamic change in body posture communicated to Tom that he has self-agency, he makes a difference in the world and in relationships, and that therefore he exists as a separate human being. Mel's nonverbal 'Yes!' *confirmed* him for being as he is. In contrast to the position, he assumed at home, he felt no need to please others within the group or imagine what we wanted. '…secretly and bashfully he watches for a Yes which allows him to be and which can come to him only from one person to another' (Buber 1965, 71).

Confirmation within a Dialogic Approach

This chapter explores *confirmation* as a component of the Gestalt *dialogic approach*, rooted in Buber's notion of 'the between' (1965). Working dialogically means bringing our whole selves into the therapeutic relationship. Not a focus on self, but rather a 'response to the client' that comes from our whole being, allowing ourselves to be moved, excited, frustrated, trusted, saddened and so on. Being with clients without expecting them to be different to how they are or to change.

DOI: 10.4324/9781003091783-13

As we work with our clients dialogically, it is crucial to be authentic and real. What do I 'experience' in you that I am confirming? In Tom's case:

I am impacted by you: *You* are powerful
I can try out following your lead: *You* have initiative
I enjoy playing alongside you: *You* are creative

I notice my responses to Tom and show by my actions that I confirm him, that his actions make a difference; therefore, he makes a difference. When this is part of an ongoing *dialogic attitude* (Hycner & Jacobs 1995, 73f), such moments contribute towards confirming his very being.

This chapter is based on our shared experiences of working with adults with learning disabilities within a National Health Service (NHS) setting. We are both trained in the Sesame approach to dramatherapy. Gillian is also a Gestalt Psychotherapist. Focusing on the group, we have been co-running for the past three years, we consider how marrying the Gestalt dialogic way of relating, with the oblique Sesame approach to dramatherapy has given us a unique perspective on our work. We consider this to be part of the development of dramatherapy practice within the field.

The key themes we explore in this chapter are:

- The term *disabled* and the cultural connotations of such a label
- The importance of raising awareness of shame, which can underlie behaviour seen by services as 'challenging'
- The impact of cultural shame
- The integration of the Gestalt dialogic approach with the Sesame Methodology
- How the dialogic approach, including confirmation, can provide an antidote to cultural shame

Vignettes from the group are used to illustrate our thoughts. The group has six members, two men and four women who range in age from late 20s to mid-50s. They came for different reasons, although each of them has been impacted by a significant change in their life. Alongside a label of learning disability, three group members also have a diagnosis of mental illness.

Cultural Connotations of the Label: 'Disabled'

In writing this chapter, we found our attention settled on the word 'dis-abled' and the negative connotation it holds. 'You are not *able* and therefore you are worth less'. This is the cultural and subliminal message that permeates the social field. It is not just our clients who are impacted by this. All of us in our culture are steeped in the message that dis-abled means missing ability and having an impairment means you are disabled.

We observe a tendency in society of making the disability *figure:* 'you are not able' becoming the focus. The qualities and personality traits of the individual become less prominent and therefore recede into the *ground* – 'the current or historical backdrop to their experience' (Joyce & Sills 2010, 26). This continues to perpetuate the superiority of those who are 'able'. We imagined the potential impact of this cultural milieu on our clients and wondered about the phenomenon of shame.

Our experience with the group is in stark contrast to these negative cultural messages. We were curious about what it is in our approach that enables a different experience. We identified it as confirming people for who they are. This does not mean ignoring the impairment – in fact, the opposite: truly seeing and validating people as they are. If we ignore the impairment, are we not putting a value judgement on what it is like to be impaired?

Confirmation is not about celebrating aspects of the individual. It is about validation. We see our role as being alongside our clients, supporting relationships to form and grow. How they bring their authentic selves to the group supports them to be true to themselves outside the group. Through this process, we are confirming their existence: This is how you live; this is how you feel, think and move; this is how you play; and it is unique to you. I delight in your individuality, and we delight in our differences.

Hycner & Jacobs (1995, 23) talk about people who do not get validation being so desperate for any confirmation, that they mould themselves into what they perceive the other wants them to be. Thus, they get confirmed for who they are not. We propose that this experience of trying to be someone you are not, and getting confirmed for it, has deep roots in shame. We believe that the culture in our society of privileging health and intellect has created a culture of shame for people who are different.

Shame and Cultural Shame

What has been our own journey with shame? What supports us to navigate the *shame territory*? We want to offer a sense of shame rooted in experience rather than just theory. We later offer a rationale for being familiar with our own shame process.

Gillian:

Growing up I sometimes felt 'bad'. I could not articulate this feeling. It was just a vague sense of being in a pit, and whatever I did to get myself out made things worse. In an exercise on the Sesame course, I was given a host of words to choose from and embody, and I made my first connection with the word shame. I gradually unpacked my phenomena of shame; feelings of being too much and yet not enough, exposed and wanting to hide, humiliation and being alone in these feelings.

Shame has not gone away. I have got to know my shame territory better. I sense the edges of the pit more sharply and can navigate the pitfalls with more skill. And, of course, there are times when I fall in. In our work together, Mel, I name this to you, and you offer me your presence. You don't try to resolve or fix. You confirm my experience. My shame exists and I exist and I make meaning from my shame experience. In the intimacy of our dialogic encounter, I climb out of my shame pit.

Mel:

As I sit down to write about my experience of shame, I realise how difficult it is. Where do I start? Do I even understand what we are talking about? How dare I think I can write about it? Who do I think I am?

I realise I feel shame. The more I try to understand it, the more lost I feel. This is my cerebral response, but as I write, I come to an image; I feel lost at sea. As a dramatherapist, metaphor is the language I know. As I feel into that image of the sea, I connect with my body. I feel overwhelmed, my head flooded, the ground beneath me swept away, I might drown. My gut tightens – a knot of humiliation, of being found out. There is also something reassuring in this land-scape. It offers a container for these feelings, placing my experience out into the wild seas that are far bigger than I am, an archetypal experience.

This is familiar territory, and over the years, through therapy, supervision and training, I have learned how to steady myself, to anchor. I know where the anchor is within my body, the size and shape of it, how to connect with it. I can then soften with my breath and sooth myself. I recognise my need for connec-tion. I reach out to you, Gillian, who, in these moments, I experience as better than me. We discover how we pass this mantle of shame back and forth as we write about it. I am not alone, I do know. My body knows, my psyche knows. I am no longer in shame.

Through describing shame from an inner place, we are modelling our *soul-imperative* (Smail 2008) as dialogic dramatherapists: bringing our embodied selves to our work. It is not how much theory we know; it is paying attention to our own process and sharing this with each other as co-therapists. Our contact provides an antidote to our own shame. We consciously include this process nonverbally with clients. When we include our whole selves, our shame as well as our self-support and relational support, we truly meet our clients with presence.

Looking at Our Own Shame

In proportion, shame serves a purpose – to develop our conscience (Kaufman 1989, 5) and to protect us when relationships are not safe. However, when shame is experienced at a more profound level, it can disable.

In our culture, the tendency to avoid feeling shame often shows up in an un-conscious desire to save face, making it hard to recognise the shame. As Evans points out, therapists cannot 'take clients through what they have not gone through themselves' (1994, 107). Working with our own shame process makes it more possible to hold the shame of our clients. We argue that there is another reason for being familiar with our own shame process, and that is to strengthen our awareness and ability to deal with the milieu of shame which permeates the field of people with learning disabilities.

Cultural Field of Learning Disabilities and Shame

'The essence of field theory is that a holistic perspective towards the person extends to include environment, the social world, organisations, culture' (Parlett 1991, 70). Our clients (like us) are interconnected with society and subject to cultural influences. Having worked in the service for many years, we have noticed the impact of being 'different' and 'dis-abled'. Cultural introjects around not being good enough can be imbibed just by belonging to the group named 'learning disabled'. Yontef (2006, 353) differentiates between 'situational shame' (responding to a specific situation) and 'existential shame', about one's global sense of self. We believe that the cultural shame around having a learning disability is existential.

Systems which uphold abuse, prevent autonomy, privilege verbal communication and have an underlying unconscious bias towards the 'mainstream population' are shameful. Shame is thus a phenomenon of the field. Where does this shame land? It should land with us as professionals, as members of society who acknowledge that people with learning disabilities are equal, valuable and contribute to society. However, 'It is not uncommon for one who is threatened with growing shame to protect oneself by attacking the other in a shame-provoking manner. This is 'shame transfer' (Jacobs 1996, 305). On a collective level, if we disown shame (often disguising it by assuming the role of expert, superior or helper), shame is likely to be transferred to people with learning disabilities who then feel, hold or act out the shame.

The Individual and the Field

Let's pick up on Tom's story. He grew up at a time when parents were encouraged to put their children into institutions, where most stayed throughout adulthood, hidden away from society. Role models within popular culture were negligible and stereotypical, so for the general population, people with learning disabilities were 'Other'.

Tom's parents chose to keep him at home. From our meetings with the family, Tom seemed deeply loved and yet he struggled with autonomy and self-agency. The referral process revealed that Tom's everyday choices were restricted.

While choosing for Tom to remain at home could be understood, at the time, as a protective act, attitudes have changed. As people with learning disabilities transition to adulthood, there is now a move towards community-based shared living, encouraging adult-to-adult relating. Yes, there is still the risk of being judged, pitied or made to feel ashamed, but responding to that fear by keeping Tom at home, in an adult-to-child relationship, could be disempowering, denying his individual choice and freedom to the detriment of his developing sense of self. Tom's history echoes the experiences of many people we have encountered through our work.

Shame is relational, and shameful attitudes towards people with disabilities are prevalent in our systems and culture. There are many examples throughout history that evidence a culture where the disabled person becomes the scapegoat, holding the collective shame of the group. Blame is placed on the individual, while the group does not hold any responsibility for attending to the underlying shame.

Shame and 'Challenging Behaviour'

The impact of shame can be hidden beneath a host of other emotions and behavioural responses, including anger, anxiety, withdrawal, self-injury, etc., and when acted out, these responses can be labelled as 'challenging behaviour'. 'Usually, it is one of the overtly displayed secondary reactions that is more easily seen and attended to by significant others. Too often shame is missed or ignored' (Kaufman 1989, 21). Our work as dramatherapists requires us to lift up this label and see what is hidden beneath. Naming the shame supports client, therapist, family and professionals to know what we are working with. We illustrate this in the vignettes below.

Fran

Fran, a woman in her late 30s, was initially referred to the service for self-harming, a behaviour that is considered 'challenging'. Through individual art therapy, Fran told her story of the trauma that lay beneath the injuries marking her body. While she had been enabled to share what had happened in her past, Fran continued to withdraw from social contact. She began experiencing her creative adjustment to withdraw as disabling. She wanted to create change in her life, and so she continued her therapeutic journey into our group.

> Fran sits in the storyteller's chair. In her arms, she cradles her doll, Rosie. Rosie supports Fran to feel safe enough to share her story with the group. Fran tells the group about Molly's arrival, a new doll, a new baby for Fran and a sister for Rosie. The group listens carefully, then, stepping forward, they recreate Fran's story. Mel swings her arms, as if cradling a baby. Fran spontaneously gets up and carries Rosie over to Mel, placing the doll in her arms, before returning to her chair to watch the drama. Mel cradles Rosie, while Eli reaches out to gently cup Rosie's head in his palm.

Mel's response:

As Fran spoke, I was reminded of her trauma history, shared during the referral process. By telling the story of her dolls, she was actually sharing something of her attempt to survive, which could leave her vulnerable to shame (Taylor 2014, 150). I felt some anxiety. She was opening a deep part of herself. This was a significant challenge and reflected her developing trust within the accepting milieu of the group.

To offer grounded support to Fran, I firstly needed to attend to myself. I pressed my feet into the floor, felt the chair behind me and breathed. I touched the anchor within me. I trusted that a spontaneous response would emerge through my body in a deeper way than my cerebral response. Fran's spontaneous act of placing the baby in my arms felt brave. Her potency was visceral. She was choosing to bring in and share the part of herself that had been shamed elsewhere. The nonverbal communication was 'here is all of me and I want to share this with you'. Holding the baby, I felt sadness and loss, yet deep love and joy. It did not matter that this was not a real baby; my emotional response was entirely real. I was trusted by Fran to hold this fragile and new part of herself. Eli reaching out to touch the baby confirmed this as a shared feeling within the group. This nonverbal and embodied offering back to Fran was an antidote to the persistent potential of shame she describes.

Over time, Fran has developed a strong ability to articulate her emotional experiences including what it is like to be seen as different. Given the history of hiding and silencing people with learning disabilities, we invited her to be interviewed (Figure 9.1).

Eli

Eli is a man in his 20s and the youngest member of the group. Alongside a visible disability, he has a speech impediment, and it can take time for Eli to find the words to express what he wants to say. Struggling to communicate verbally has led to feelings of fear, anxiety and powerlessness.

One of Eli's reasons for referral was to develop confidence in using his voice and communicate his choices clearly to other people. Although we are not allowed to share details due to confidentiality, we were aware he had experienced a disempowering trauma while in supported accommodation, which further impacted on his ability to self-advocate.

Throughout the shame literature, a correlation is drawn between powerlessness and shame. '*Powerlessness* in any sphere of life, because it is an impediment and therefore thwarts positive affect, activates shame' (Kaufman 1989, 56).

The following vignette is taken from a session when Eli worked with the theme of power.

Having heard the story, 'The Queen and the Lute' (Johnson 1996, 86f), the group is invited to choose a role to play in the story enactment. Choosing the Queen, Eli holds the purple velvet fabric ready for action. It is the fabric he chooses each session, and the group has come to recognise the importance of it for him. He is engrossed in the action of the drama that unfolds. In the 'bridge out' from the enactment, the part of the Sesame session structure where the unconscious experience is brought into a more conscious space (Smail 2013, 56)

Interview with Fran:	Comments
G: You bring your dolls to our sessions; how might they help you? F: They help me to sort of be in the group. Settle and be able to take part in things.	One of our aims for the group has been to cultivate a culture of acceptance. Fran's doll(s) are an important form of support that enable her to come into the group. From the outset we dialogued with Fran, co-creating the support needed to include her dolls in sessions. As we recognise and respond to her dolls as emerging aspects of herself, we are confirming her creative ways of surviving in the world.
M: We have talked about when you take your babies to the park. What is it like when you do this? F: Gives you a satisfaction that you are not alone. It means you can be independent. You know, nobody isn't going to know what they are if you don't tell them so you don't get judged. It is comforting.	Whilst offering essential support, the dolls also invite the potential for shaming. An adult seen in the park with dolls could be met with derision; dolls are toys for children. Fran knows this and expresses her fear of being judged. If the babies are recognised as dolls, there is the threat of being rejected.
M: What sort of reactions do you get from people? F: They ask how old they are. I make up an age. M: Do they think you are a mum? F: Yes G: How does that make you feel? F: Sometimes it makes me feel good and sometimes I want to tell them what they are, but I am too scared because sometimes people can judge you for pushing these types of dolls around.	The dolls could be seen as a creative adjustment that allow Fran an experience of being mother; an aspect of self that is often denied by society for people with a learning disability. The role of mother holds value in our society. Potentially the underlying threat of 'being found out' for not really being a mother creates fear of being shamed. "If you put Shame in a Dish, it needs three things to grow exponentially: Secrecy, silence and judgment." (Brene Brown)
M: Are they a comfort to you when you are out? F: Yes. I have got to take them with me everywhere I go. M: So, you don't go anywhere without your babies? F: I don't go nowhere without a baby.	The dolls provide a creative way for Fran to self-regulate, in direct contrast to the attacks inflicted upon herself through self-harm. Rather than recreating the suffering through an attack upon self that can be seen as an embodied message of 'I am bad', she uses the dolls as an antidote to her deep shame. She holds them, they hold her. Whilst there is fear of shaming ridicule for taking her dolls out into the world, Fran has the strength to do this anyway and continues to find safe ways to adjust and adapt.
G: Do you remember telling the story of when you got Molly and the group acted it out for you? F: Yes, I do remember that. M: what was it like to see me holding your baby in that drama? F: It makes me feel good when people hold them and look after them and respect them. I felt really proud that I handed over something so precious to me. M: I felt really trusted by you to hold Rosie.	The group has offered her ways to own her need for the dolls, rather than feeling as though they need to be hidden away. No value judgment is put onto the dolls. They are seen, welcome and celebrated, just as each group member is.
G: I remember Eli gently touched Rosie's head. How was that for you? F: I thought it was that he was trying to interact with her. I don't mind him holding them and touching them because he might like the feel of them and the touch of them and want one himself.	Fran experiences Eli's actions as showing curiosity and interest, seeing that she has something to offer that is of value to others. This in turn allows an experience of feeling her own value and sense of self-worth.

Figure 9.1 Interview with Fran.

Gillian asks each group member, as their character, to place their hand on their heart and answer:

G: What is your heart's desire?

*E: The scarf (*indicating the purple fabric*)*

G: I am really curious about the scarf, you love the scarf

*E: My voice... (*very long pause) .... *to shout...* (long pause) .... *power.*

It takes time for Eli to respond. The group waits. No one guesses or suggests what words he is trying to form. There is a sense of acceptance of Eli and his speech impairment, a feeling of space and time. We are confirming him for who he is, as he finds the words that state his experience and feeling of power.

> Gillian invites Eli to turn to the group and shout; to embody what has been spoken. Putting on the fabric, Eli turns, lifts his arm towards Mel and very clearly and loudly says her name. This is followed by a commanding gesture, palm outstretched and a strong growling sound. Next, he turns to Fran, calling her name, repeating his actions. After allowing time for this to be felt and held within the group, Gillian invites Eli to step out of the fabric while still holding the power within his heart. As he does this, Gillian repeats the phrase 'You are powerful' to Eli.
>
> In the sessions that follow, Eli continues to work with the purple fabric, revisiting and repeating the sound and movement described above. In each role he chooses, we see him connecting with his power, expressed through the different characters. This is seen, witnessed and echoed back by the group.

Our intention in this group is to create a culture that provides an antidote to shame. The framework of the Sesame approach supports a milieu where Eli can exercise freedom of choice and self-agency. He embodies the character, feeling his power nonverbally, and then begins to communicate his emerging awareness. Gillian's invitation to name and embody his experiences marries the indirect Sesame approach with Gestalt: 'Gestalt as a dialogic encounter seeks a relationship in which power is horizontal (equal)…and that treats the other as a person and not as an object to be manipulated or controlled' (Yontef 1991). 'It emphasizes a mutuality of contact that gently and respectfully calls the person out of isolation. As the person's inner self comes out of hiding and emerges into awareness, […shame] is gradually replaced with curiosity, excitement and eventually love' (Evans 1994, 105). Here, both approaches are needed, to enable Eli to make contact with his power and share this experience with the group. As Smail describes (2000), it is the space and time allowed by the oblique nature of the Sesame approach that enables the unconscious to become conscious. Eli revisits and re-experiences this archetypal motif, choosing the same fabric, making the same movements and repeating the words 'power' and 'voice' in the weeks that follow. Working primarily nonverbally, he stays with this process that allows the safe unveiling of his new experience of self. We come alongside Eli within the drama, to carefully support him to develop his relationship with this new emergent part of self.

> we accompany our clients on the journey they make; we stand alongside them, and, without judgement, are curious and empathic in our responses to the path they travel. We support our clients in locating and accessing the guide, the wise person, the helper. We witness this process and affirm their ability to manage and embrace change.
>
> (Mann Shaw & Gammage 2011, 141)

While communicating verbally can be incredibly difficult for Eli, he is fluent in the language of movement and his nonverbal expression of his emotional experience is striking. The very nature of the Sesame approach, where emphasis is placed on nonverbal interaction, confirms Eli.

Conclusion

We have considered the psychological and emotional impact of shame and how this can be experienced as loss of power and voice and as an inhibiting behaviour. Although attitudes have changed, we still observe the projection of cultural shame onto those labelled learning dis-abled, where, 'You should be ashamed of who you are' continues to be a subliminal message. To manage the shame-response, creative adjustments are needed.

How people creatively adjust depends on how their unique field conditions, including life experience, living conditions, class, race and culture, are configured. Archetypal roles such as the 'Pleaser' can emerge in response to implied messages such as 'We'll accept you as long as you please us'. This can lead to people with learning disabilities living a false self and getting confirmed for who they are *not*.

We see dramatherapy as an opportunity to create a new cultural milieu of acceptance, a place to experiment with being who you are and exploring what that means for you. We offer spaces for play: playing with ways of being in the world, playing to deepen relationships and playing to discover our authentic selves.

Our work takes place within an NHS setting where shame is a phenomenon of the field. We see our role as directly challenging this culture and promoting the confirmation of our clients. To do so, it is integral that we are embedded within the system. Alongside therapy, we offer group supervision, reflective practice and consultation. This is where we can bring shame into professional awareness and encourage ownership, thus reducing projection of shame onto people who have a learning disability.

We want to end this chapter thinking about Tom, Fran and Eli. As they tentatively try out discovering and being themselves, we confirm them, confirm their very existence, 'Yes, you are!'

References

Buber, M. 1926/1965. *Between Man and Man* (trans. R.G. Smith). New York: The Macmillan (Original works published in 1926, 1929, 1936, 1938 & 1939).

Evans, K.R. 1994. 'Healing Shame: A Gestalt Perspective'. In: *British Gestalt Journal,* 24 (2): 103–108. London and Cardiff: Gestalt Publications Ltd.

Hycner, R. & Jacobs, L. 1995. *The Healing Relationship in Gestalt Therapy*. Gouldsboro, ME: Gestalt Journal Press.

Jacobs, L. 1996. 'Shame in the Therapeutic Dialogue'. In Lee, R.G. & Wheeler, G. Eds. *The Voice of Shame: Silence and Connection in Psychotherapy*, 297–314. San Francisco, CA: Jossey-Bass.

Johnston, A. 1996. *Eating in the Light of the Moon: How Women Can Transform Their Relationship with Food through Myths, Metaphors and Storytelling.* Carlsbad: Gúrze Books.

Joyce, P. & Sills, C. 2010. *Skills in Gestalt Counselling and Psychotherapy.* London: Sage Publications Ltd.

Kaufman, G. 1989. *The Psychology of Shame: Theory and Treatment of Shame-Based Syndromes.* New York: Springer.

Mann, D. 2010. *Gestalt Therapy: 100 Key Points and Techniques.* London and New York: Routledge.

Mann Shaw, S. & Gammage, D. 2011. 'The Drama of Shame'. In *Dramatherapy,* 33 (3): 131–143. London: Routledge.

Parlett, M. 1991. 'Reflections on Field Theory'. In: *The British Gestalt Journal,* 1 (2): 69–81. London and Cardiff: Gestalt Publications Ltd.

Smail, M. 2000. *Sesame Training in Drama and Movement Therapy.* London: [Royal] Central School of Speech and Drama: *Personal communication.*

Smail, M. 2008. *Psyche and Soma Training.* Cardiff: *Personal Communication.*

Smail, M. 2013. 'Entering and Leaving the Place of Myth'. In Pearson, J., Smail, M. & Watts, P. Eds. *Dramatherapy with Myth and Fairytale: The Golden Stories of Sesame,* 55–72. London: Jessica Kingsley Publishers.

Taylor, M. 2014. *Trauma Therapy and Clinical Practice: Neuroscience, Gestalt and the Body.* New York: Open University Press.

Yontef, G. 1991. 'Recent Trends in Gestalt Therapy in the United States and What We Need to Learn from Them'. In: *British Gestalt Journal,* 1: 5–20. London and Cardiff: Gestalt Publications Ltd.

Yontef, G. 2006. 'Shame and Guilt in Gestalt Therapy: Theory and Practice'. In: Lee, R.G. & Wheeler, G. Eds. *The Voice of Shame: Silence and Connection in Psychotherapy,* 351–380. San Francisco, CA: Jossey-Bass.

Chapter 10

Attunement in Dramatherapy

Working Intuitively and the Importance of the Co-Working Relationship

Tim Goldman and Lina Ib

Introduction

In a North London day centre, two therapists embarked on a one-year dramatherapy project for adults with learning disabilities. The project was run by Roundabout, the largest dramatherapy charity in the UK, who had been providing dramatherapy at the centre over a number of years.

This chapter focuses on how an intuitive approach to facilitation can develop and strengthen group cohesion and create a unique base from which to express, explore and play together.

Reflecting on this work, we found there were two significant areas that were fundamental to how the therapy progressed and how the group evolved:

- The power of 'Attunement': to mentally align to another being
- The dynamics of co-facilitation: 'working together'

This chapter explores the different facets of attunement, from how we as drama-therapists attuned in different ways to the clients, and vice versa; how the thera-pists' attunement to each other guided the work; and how the clients themselves attuned to each other. It also explores the many benefits of co-working: essentially that the therapists take on different roles, for example, one can take a more active role while the other can observe. This facilitation style became integral to the process itself. This chapter describes the methods and techniques that we used and examines how an intuitive or spontaneous approach, allied to a sense of fun, allowed the group to develop its own personality and prepared us to explore more deeply when the moment was right.

Our Group

The group, made up of six participants, was set up through an established referral system. Referrals were made by the centre manager, who had spoken with the service users about dramatherapy. The group comprised four men and two women between the ages of 30 and 60 years. It was run as a closed group to create a safe

DOI: 10.4324/9781003091783-14

space for the individuals to share and express themselves freely and to use the opportunity to form trusting relationships between each other and with the therapists.

Reasons for referral included high anxiety, shyness, social isolation, bereavement, low self-esteem and mood swings. Some of the group members had additional diagnoses to their learning disability, such as autism, Down's syndrome and mental health issues. All the group members chose to communicate verbally: four could be described as introverted and quiet with more limited language, while two were more extrovert and able to communicate more freely. They all suffered anxiety to different degrees. Three of the participants had lost a family member shortly before attending the group, and one man lost his father during the project. Although their needs were quite different, they shared an eagerness to attend and a commitment to the group.

The therapeutic alliance included the option of sitting out an activity and witnessing the group rather than participating. Group members seemed to find this supportive, while we felt it contributed to the high level of attendance. It was important to encourage and promote a sense of self-agency, as people with learning disabilities may not feel it within themselves, often not being aware of the possibility of being able to make a choice (Chesner 1995).

This project was evaluated using the *Psychlops LD*. This learning disability evaluation is a pilot based on work being developed through Roundabout's 'Psychlop Kids' project (Haythorne et al. 2012). Questionnaires were given to the participants before and after attending the group. Evaluation of the project was important as we wanted to assess the impact of the sessions and to provide evidence that dramatherapy is an effective clinical intervention for people with learning disabilities.

Methods and Techniques

The dramatherapy group was held every week and took place in the morning shortly after the opening of the centre. Members would sit in a circle, allowing us all to be seen equally. As therapists, we usually sat opposite each other to pick up on each other's cues while running the group. Each week, the sessions followed the same structure to provide a sense of safety and familiarity through ritual and repetition. The sessions comprised a mix of planned exercises and story work that was developed from the group's engagement with previous sessions, which might include more improvised activity depending on the mood of the group. With this group, we felt it was important to have slightly looser boundaries to reduce the high levels of anxiety around being late or doing something wrong, as described by Valarie Sinason (Corbett 2019). It helped us to facilitate the group with respect, warmth, kindness and curiosity.

As the group were settling, a ball would be passed around the circle and then we focused inwardly on our breathing. This was followed by a check-in, when group members were invited to share how they were feeling, in a way that was comfortable for them: verbally, through movement or in any other creative way. Warming up exercises often involved mirroring, where the group would take turns to lead and copy movements of the others. This provided an opportunity for the group members to take time noticing each other, build empathy, connection and to feel seen. Winnicott (1967) identifies this 'mirroring' as a developmental process that occurs between children and their caregivers and which promotes relationships generally.

A main activity and focus of the session then followed. Depending on the needs, interests and choice of the group, this might be a story and enactment, improvisation, art activity or the creation of a group poem. To bring this activity to a conclusion, the group members were helped to leave their imaginative worlds and return to the here and now, by using a de-role exercise. For example, by each person naming the character, they had been in the story enactment and then stating their own name. To help prepare for the rest of their day, the group liked to share a song, accompanied by one of the dramatherapists on the ukulele.

Sessions were planned with the benefit of participant feedback from the previous week, which helped us understand the therapeutic needs and significant themes of the group. The main impetus, however, was one of encouraging a sense of freedom and the acceptance of each individual's needs and personality. We aimed to create a feeling of fun and connection, while improvising within a safe structure. Most members of the group were confident and trusting enough to offer suggestions for what to do in the moment. These suggestions were acknowledged and valued, giving the group a sense of being heard and having choices, which is so important. People with learning disabilities often experience a sense of not being heard and have little control over their own lives.

All the participants had struggled with feelings of low self-worth and not being good enough, so the main goal of the therapy was to offer each person a sense of feeling celebrated and appreciated for who they were. The aim was for the dramatherapy sessions to be a space where each person could engage with moments of feeling free without any sense of shame or judgement.

As dramatherapy is a playful and creative approach, it can offer a reparative therapeutic experience, where participants have the opportunity to experience the healing aspects of childhood play, which they may have missed out on previously. This process is akin to how parents play with their children in attuned parenting, connecting to each other through the play, creating an atmosphere of each person feeling seen and appreciated (Siegel & Hartzell 2003).

As therapists, we participated in the exercises, all of us collaborating as a group. We witnessed how our 'joining in' enabled the participants to do so too. When we showed that we were willing to take risks, demonstrate vulnerability or be silly, the group participants were more confident in embracing the different aspects of themselves and entered into the session more fully. Ultimately, there needed to be a sense of safety and trust within the group that would enable free play and spontaneity.

On reflection, the most important aspect of the therapy in building relationships and trust was the process of 'attunement'.

Attunement

To attune to someone is to allow our state of mind to align with that of another. It is the process by which we form relationships. It is when:

> a person, a parent for example, focuses their attention on the internal world of another. This focus on the mind of another person harnesses neural circuity that enable two people to 'feel felt' by each other. This state is crucial for people in relationships to feel vibrant and alive, to feel understood and to feel at peace.
>
> (Siegal 2007, 1)

When we connect with the emotions of another person, we can experience a sense of feeling joined. By connecting with their emotions, we are also more able to see things from their point of view. Our recognising why a person might be feeling a certain way can help that person feel more emotionally regulated, because they experience a sense of being 'seen' and understood.

Our attunement was linked to our 'intuitive function' as we sensed the feelings of each group member while we facilitated the sessions. We developed an understanding of whether we needed to stop and take time to be in a certain moment or to move on to the next part of the session. When the attunement resonated well, we found a fluidity where each part of the session followed the next in a way that felt truly person centred.

VIGNETTE 1

One male client presented as being very much alone in his own imaginative world, often moving or dancing in the space, eyes closed, accompanying himself by making sounds. Within the context of the group exercise, which was focused on noticing each other and attuning together, we were able to support his interest in and engagement with others, by one of the therapists attuning to and mirroring his movements and sounds. His creative expression could then more easily be incorporated into the main action of the group.

One such session saw many of us spontaneously, following his lead, become birds with a sense of having wings. This process of attuning with the client enabled him to engage with other group members and change for himself from an inward to an outward focus. This in turn created a space that changed the activity of the group letting them move on and develop.

Reflecting on our work with this group, many aspects were significant, but the consistent thread was the nature of the connections within the group. Our attunement as therapists ran parallel to our attunement with the clients and the clients' attunement with each other. These processes enabled the group to connect with their own inner resources, giving them confidence to take part, try something new, share difficulties and build relationships.

Bloom (2006) writes about an 'embodied attentiveness', how connecting nonverbally and engaging with psychophysical states enhances the therapist's ability to attune to that which may be felt but is not yet thought or verbalised. Reading the signals within a group can be a challenge as so many processes occur simultaneously. Over time, we began to understand the less-verbal members by where and how they sat and how relaxed their bodies appeared to be and from their eye contact with us. Often a group member would need more involved attention from one of us, while the other would continue to facilitate the action of the session. Staying with, and giving space to, an individual's challenging emotions can be difficult, and having a co-facilitator was very helpful to us being able to maintain the flow of the session, while giving space for individual emotional needs.

Attunement between Therapist and Client

As the group arrived at the session, the rapid assessment process helped us attune to the emotional presentation of each member. Some would bring similar issues to the start of every session, creating opportunities for the therapists to attend to their stories. For example, one member often needed time to speak of his difficult and unsettling journey to the centre, and another needed space to share his urgent worries and anxieties before he could join the session.

Chodorow (1991) describes how Jung would sit opposite his clients so that they could see each other, in a process that was different to the more traditional Freudian approach, 'When therapist and patient can be seen by each other, psychotherapy re-institutes the mirroring that is so fundamental to the parent and infant relationship' (Chodorow, 144).

Members could join in with the creative exercises in any way they felt most comfortable with. Several group members felt movement, and working with their bodies was a more comfortable way of connecting. Attunement within the group supported relationship building through different ways of communicating. When language is more limited, therapy is less about cognition than about relating (Corbett 2009). Cynthia Berrol (2006) recommends physical activities such as drumming and singing, which use rhythms that are consistent with a heartbeat, as they help build the brain's ability to sustain attention and create attunement by activating both hemispheres of the brain. Connecting to others through movement can lead to an increased empathy for the other.

Working with stories, both traditional and created in the moment, can also support a real freedom of expression.

VIGNETTE 2

When using stories, one man frequently chose to play animal characters and would improvise his part on the fringe of the group and outside the main action. If he was open to it, the therapists would try to join in with him and create a bridge between him, the rest of the group and the focus of the story. We would do this by mirroring some of his actions and assimilate his contribution into the main narrative of the story. In one session, he made a spontaneous offer of being a plane, and this led to an improvised story of a group trip to Australia, in which he took the role of the pilot. He often chose to be a little separate from the group, but the choices he made related to the story and demonstrated his interest in connecting with others and sometimes taking the lead. Following this session, he chose to share a more personal story and talked about his family in Turkey and of missing them. It opened up a space for others to share feelings around missing family members. This vignette demonstrates the value in using a shared creative experience to build emotional connection.

The group experience of each other was highly valuable, but the energy and presentation of the therapists themselves also impacted on the energy, mood and attunement of the group.

VIGNETTE 3

One group member presented as very self-conscious when he felt put on the spot. In the verbal check-in, he would consistently state that he felt 'fine'. However, he demonstrated a far wider range of expressions, when he was able to communicate using a musical instrument or through movement.

The therapists picked up on this theme and introduced the story of The Musicians of Bremen. One of the therapists deliberately took up the story with energy and confidence, and this client attuned to the therapist and unexpectedly took on a lead role of the 'Rooster' with the therapists' support. Together they expressed the character through sound and movement with confidence and boldness. The client appeared to love being involved in the story and connected with the therapists. This increased sense of agency and confidence continued when he chose to create scenery for the stories out of fabrics.

The gentle, gradual building of trust between him and the therapists, and him and the group, supported him to take risks and express different parts of himself. It's about adapting to the client, moment by moment, and finding creative ways for them to express themselves more fully.

As therapists, we felt the benefits of the process lasting for a whole year, which allowed for a little less pressure on ourselves to 'understand' or 'achieve' and more time to listen and give time.

VIGNETTE 4

All the group members benefitted from allowing time and not being rushed. One woman especially needed time during the check-in. Once she was warmed up, she enjoyed commanding the group to listen to her. At other times when she sought attention, the therapists and the other group members gave her space. This could lead to vocal outbursts and hilarity, which some of the group join in with while others just observed. At these times, the dramatherapist sitting closest might move closer, offer to gently hold her hand or join in with the hilarity, while the other therapist would sensitively attune into the rest of the group to see how they were reacting and notice if anyone was becoming lost at this moment. A similar situation, on another day, might have had a different therapist intervention, depending on the atmosphere in the room and the individual moods of the participants.

In one session, this client arrived feeling upset. The focus of the session that week was the story of Persephone. She chose to act as the lead character, and the female therapist took on the role of her mother, Demeter, and their connection transformed the atmosphere very quickly. The close bond between them was intensified by the powerful focus of the client towards the therapist – mother and daughter acting out the emotion in the story so truthfully. Simultaneously, the rest of the group engaged, verbally and nonverbally, with the emotions expressed. The group attuned to the relationship being enacted and recognised and valued the energy she had brought to the session. As things progressed through the year, she became more vocal, laughing out loud, and more open about sharing her feelings towards her home and family. Being more at ease in these later sessions, we saw signs of the 'Trickster' archetype in her story enactments, showing that she had grown comfortable in showing these different aspects of her personality. There was also a genuine warmth shown as she initiated holding hands with both therapists and clients.

Group Members Attuning to Each Other

For group members to be able to attune to each other takes time to develop and results from the choice and agency of the group members, as well as the skills and alignment of the co-facilitators. The creative work itself (movement work and stories) can support a meaningful connection between the clients that might lead to a greater sense of attunement and empathy between people.

To emphasise this within our particular group, the co-facilitators tried to coordinate the different states of introversion/extroversion within the group. There were times when a more vocal or energetic approach created a togetherness in the group, usually in a role-playing scene or vocal warm-up. At other times, the group would attune to each other during a quiet or silent dynamic, for example, when holding hands in the circle or listening to a group soundscape.

VIGNETTE 5

The most active and vocal member of the group was a man, whose outgoing attitude towards others played a big part in the whole group becoming comfortable with one another. For him, it was important to speak about the difficulties and worries he had experienced since the last session. He found the sound and movement work at the beginning of each session really fun and embraced the opportunity; his confidence and creativity being a spark for others. Occasionally, he worked with a quiet member of the group, and their attunement led to this quieter person finding a confidence and a sense of fun they had struggled to express before. Together they created a positive energy, and the offer was taken up by the more reserved of the two. In these moments, he found his voice and his body. As the group continued to attune to each other over time, they became more comfortable in sharing their life experiences, and they became increasingly supportive of each other.

In this particular group, there was a shared experience of bereavement; three individuals had been recently bereaved before joining the group, and another group member lost his father after joining the group. As trust grew between them, the group were able to support each other and work on this important theme, both in verbal sharing and in creative work. Stories, such as 'The day the sea went out and never came back', and the traditional stories of 'The Angel's Wing's' and 'The White Bird' were all used to work indirectly on themes of loss and dying. The use of stories allowed each individual to experience a sense of not being alone with their loss, both from the narrative of the stories and from the reflections of the others in the group. Different elements were often added to the stories by group members which led to more sharing and reflection. One of the quieter members of the group was able to recognise the finality of her mother's death, through building an understanding of shared experience. Instead of speaking of how she would see her mother 'later', as she had at the start of therapy, she began to speak of her mother not being here anymore and could speak of feeling sad. Supported by, and attuned to, the group, she held her hands to her heart as she shared her feelings with the group.

The Co-Working Therapist Relationship

Prior to this project, the two dramatherapists had worked together for a number of years. We found that we both aimed to work in a way that was fully present, yet free and spontaneous at any given moment of a session. For any group to feel trusting in the therapy process, they needed to have trust that the co-facilitating relationship is respectful and authentic. 'Robust co-facilitation lays the groundwork for meaningful interpersonal attunement' (Wise & Nash 2020, xxii).

Although our personalities differ, one of us being more extrovert and outgoing and the other quieter and reflective, we fundamentally share an openness, warmth and playfulness. Through supervision, we have come to appreciate how instead of trying to be more like the other, having different personality types allows us more scope to connect with the varying and changing needs of the group. Our different styles can be seen to complement each other as described by MacDonald (2020).

Carson (2020) states that good co-facilitation is like joining in a rhythmic, shared dance.

Attunement prior to the start of the session became an important ritual: palm to palm facing each other and breathing together or in a more physical way through a dance to find the right energy for a given session. This helped prepare us to welcome each person, and to find the right times to spark off each other creatively during the sessions, responding in the moment.

VIGNETTE 6

One of the men in the group was particularly unpredictable in his temperament from week to week. As co-facilitators we needed to be sensitive to this and quickly attune to his needs. This could vary from him either taking time out from the session and only joining when feeling calmer or he might be very jovial, saying how much he enjoyed the group.

The therapists devoted time to connecting to him, one of us sitting beside him or staying with him for a little while outside of the room. This demonstrated to the group as a whole our positive attunement each week, which helped them to understand him better and to warm to him. He had always apparently found it difficult to make close friendships, and in the early weeks, he was visibly frustrated by other members of the group. He was given the opportunity over these sessions to develop positive relationships and to play characters which supported him to relate more directly with others in the group.

He was often paired up with the other more vocal members of the group and in one session spoke of how he 'liked being his friend'. It was noticeable how his eye contact and demeanour changed over time and how the ongoing dialogue in his head (which he often vocalised) diminished when he was more engaged with the group.

Many in the group had experienced trauma and could be quickly impacted by other's moods. They might be worried and express concern if someone arrived upset and would retreat within themselves if they felt overwhelmed by someone else's emotional expression. Co-facilitation created more room for the safe expression of these feelings and a chance to model attuned support and encourage group members to support one another. Yalom (1995) proposes that the stronger the co-facilitation relationship, the more likely the group members are to experience a corrective emotional experience. The members of a group experience their place within it, and their relationship with the therapists, in ways that are affected by early attachment experiences. Attachment is the lasting bond that connects one person to another across time and space (Bowlby 1969). Early attachment patterns can be played out in group processes. Rom and Mikulincer (2003) found that an anxious or avoidant attachment style affected behaviours in a group setting. For example, an anxious pattern of attachment led to individuals seeking more closeness and the approval of others, while an avoidant style meant a person's participation was more distant. Cohesion and a sense of safety and flow within the group had a significant effect on reducing the effects of attachment anxiety. While facilitating the group, it was important for us to attune to these different attachment patterns.

One female tended to move from being distant with the group, seeming to be preoccupied with her own thoughts, to being more connected. To support her with feeling comfortable and being able to attend the session, we needed to carefully attune to her changing moods and needs. For example, giving her space and reducing eye contact when needed.

When a person showed a more anxious attachment pattern, as described in Vignette 6, we attuned in ways that would support them in feeling more grounded and regulated, by one of us sitting close and having gentle contact or doing an exercise alongside them.

As therapists we modelled a functioning, healthy relationship where we took turns, treated each other with respect, valued each other's input and had an open dialogue. This sense of cohesion from the therapists and connection with the group creates a secure base (Bowlby 1988), from which the group can move on.

We believe that having a male and female therapist was a helpful representation for the group, for projective and potentially reparative work.

VIGNETTE 7

The female therapist found herself put into the role of carer/mother by two of the women in the group when they sought support at times of heightened emotion, as described in vignette 4. One of the women had recently lost her mother and would naturally seek the therapist's reassurance. The other female had been brought up without her mother and was living with her father. This woman had a more avoidant attachment style, as described above. The female therapist would sit near to her, and by using a gentle touch support her through a shared silence or by providing a gentle, quiet commentary on what was happening in the space. In these moments, the therapist was able to attune to the individual freely, while the other therapist held the group. Activities such as clapping or singing could also bring the client back in attunement with the others. During a drama enactment, the therapists might swap in and out of role to be along-side the client and support her to stay engaged and facilitate her interest in taking part.

Attunement between therapists takes focus and intention. By working this way, therapists can help each other get back into being attuned to the group; for example, if one is becoming disconnected by external concerns, like some-one uninvited entering the room, the other therapist can give space for them to come back and take the lead with the group. It is a process of shifting, chang-ing and moving (Wise & Nash 2020).

Reflection, debriefing and supervision allowed us to share thoughts on mo-ments and interactions from the sessions, hearing the other person's experi-ence and letting this feed into planning the next session.

Concluding Thoughts

Dramatherapy has proved to be a stimulating approach for this client group, and having a whole year together provided space for individuals to find their own jour-ney and by the end be very much part of a dynamic and caring group. Together we were creative, we listened and helped everyone to attune to each other in their own time. The therapeutic relationship was crucial in the establishment of trust and friendship.

In addition to this, the co-facilitating style of the therapists offered a mutual understanding of how to work in this type of setting and the confidence and spon-taneity that was to be mirrored by the group. As individuals became increasingly involved in the sessions as the weeks progressed, a more sensitive attunement de-veloped and a sense of being more alive grew within the group,

The structure of the dramatherapy programme gave a sense of holding, while the therapists flexible, intuitive, spontaneous approach supported the individual needs and aims for the group members as they emerged. The relational approach of dramatherapy and our client-centred approach led to growth and change.

This chapter ends with the voices of the group members, who gave feedback and completed the Psychlops LD evaluation after attending the project.

The evaluation had a very positive outcome with an effect size of 1.64. An ef-fect size over 1 is considered to be high and demonstrates that an intervention has worked. Below are some of the reflections from the group members:

'We were a nice group and we are better friends now'.

'I really enjoyed myself. I wish they would come back. I loved dramatherapy'.

'I'm glad I did it. I feel better now'.

'I miss the dramatherapists. What we gonna do without them? They were nice and patient'.

It is with great fondness that we reflect on this project and remember the individuals who participated in the group. Dramatherapy gave them a space, and they found new voices to fill it.

References

Berrol, C.F. 2006. 'Neuroscience meets dance/movement therapy: Mirror neurons, the therapeutic process and empathy'. In: *The Arts in Psychotherapy*, Volume 33, Issue 4, 302–315. Science Direct Online.

Bloom, K. 2006. *The Embodied Self. Movement and Psychoanalysis*. London: Karnac.

Bowlby, J. 1969. *Attachment. Attachment and Loss Volume 1. Loss*. New York: Basic Books.

Bowlby, J. 1988. *A Secure Base, Clinical Applications of Attachment Theory*. Abingdon: Routledge.

Carson, G.D. 2020. 'Greater than the sum of its parts: The value of co-led trauma group psychotherapy'. In: Wise, S. & Nash, E. (eds.) *Healing Trauma in Group Settings: The Art of Co-Leader Attunement*, 102–127. New York: Routledge.

Chesner, A. 1995. *Dramatherapy for People with Learning Disabilities: A World of Difference*. London: Jessica Kingsley Publishers.

Chodorow, J. 1991. *Dance Therapy and Depth Psychology, the Moving Imagination*. London: Routledge.

Corbett, A. 2009. 'Words as a second language: The psychotherapeutic challenge of severe intellectual disability'. In: Cottis, T. (ed.) *Intellectual Disability, Trauma and Psychotherapy* (45–62). New York: Routledge.

Corbett, A. 2019. *An Interview with Valerie Sinason Reflecting on Her Life and the Evolution of Disability Psychotherapy in Intellectual Disability and Psychotherapy.* (173–185). Abingdon: Routledge.

Haythorne, D., Crockford, S. & Godfrey, E. 2012. 'Roundabout and the development of PYSCHLOPS Kids evaluation'. In: Leigh, L., Giersch, I., Dix, A. & Haythorne, D. (eds.) *Dramatherapy with Children, Young People and Schools Enabling Creativity, Sociability, Communication on and Learning*, 185–194. London: Routledge.

MacDonald, S. 2020. 'Co-leading trauma groups across disciplines'. In Wise, S. & Nash, E. (Eds.) *Healing Trauma in Group Settings, The Art of Co-Leader Attunement*, 90–101. New York: Routledge.

Rom, E. & Mikulincer, M. 2003. 'Attachment theory and group processes: The association between attachment style and group-related representations, goals, memories, and functioning'. In: *Journal of Personality and Social Psychology*, Volume 84, Issue 6, 1220–1235. Interaction Design Foundation Online.

Siegal, D.J. 2007. *Reflections on the Mindful Brain, a Brief Overview Adapted from The Mindful Brain: Reflection and Attunement in the Cultivation of Wellbeing.* New York: WW Norton.

Siegel, D.J. & Hartzell, M. 2003. *Parenting from the Inside out: How a Deeper Understanding Can Help You Raise Children Who Thrive.* New York: Penguin Group.

Sunderland, M. 2003. *The Day the Sea Went out and Never Came Back.* London: SpeechMark Publishing LTD.

Winnicott, D.W. 1967. *Mirror role of Child and Family in Child Development, Playing and Reality.* London. Routledge: Classics 2005.

Wise, S. & Nash, E. 2020. *Healing Trauma in Group Settings: The Art of Co-Leader Attunement.* New York: Routledge.

Yalom, I.D. 1995. *The Theory and Practice of Group Psychotherapy.* New York: Basic books.

Chapter 11

Meeting the Challenge

Co-Producing a Presentation as an Evaluation Process

Seren Haf Grime

Introduction

This chapter reflects on my practice as a dramatherapist in the National Health Service (NHS), in a specialist-intensive service that fed into an Assessment and Treatment Unit (ATU), multidisciplinary team (MDT): a service for adults who have a learning disability and mental health problems. This chapter focuses on Cherie's story. Cherie has given her consent for her name to be used, for me to write about the process and for it to be published. Cherie has a moderate learning disability and was labelled as 'challenging' within the service.

During the evaluation process, Cherie told me she would like to tell people about the outcomes of the dramatherapy sessions. We conceived the idea of co-producing a presentation. Together we presented it at local and national conferences, telling her story on stage. A clear timeline of our story can be seen in Figure 11.1.

In this chapter, I consider how and why, through the dramatherapy process, Cherie was empowered to request and be confident enough to perform a presentation on stage.

This chapter focuses on the evaluation process and demonstrates that together we measured how aims were met and acknowledged when it was the right time to propose a presentation at a local conference.

Cherie

Cherie was born in the late 1970s. By 1983, the government was committed to their 'Care in the Community' policy, which aimed to de-institutionalise care and keep individuals in their own home. Cherie lived at home with her parents and was an active participant in social events provided in the local community. She was born on the hospital site where we had a clinical space and had lived in the town all her life. She would always bump into someone she knew at the shops or at the doctors and discuss local gossip at length. She had a long-term relationship in her 20s with a male, and she spent time with him at the farm which was a local day service. Later in her life, she cared for her father and then for her mother. For Cherie's 40th birthday, the community nurse, who had known Cherie and her family since she was born, helped her to organise her party.

DOI: 10.4324/9781003091783-15

Timeline	Provision	Cherie's journey	Focus in Chapter
2011	The service had a behavioural focus, employing a team of Behaviour Clinical Specialists (BCS), Occupational Therapist and a Clinical Psychologist. Cherie was referred for: • Service model: 3 week assessment and brief 12 week intervention (capacity was protected to cover a large geographical area). • No Dramatherapist in the Arts Therapies Community Team • No Dramatherapy provision available on discharge from ATU	Cherie refused to engage at this time	See Analytical Snapshot: Beginning
2012-2013	Assessment, Intervention and Review • Recommendations of the MDT for long term Dramatherapy. • Long term dramatherapy not possible within the current service model • Application to the Continuing Health Care (CHC) funding team for a Dramatherapist to be funded for 40 sessions.	Cherie engaged with the process with the dramatherapist Cherie requested long term Dramatherapy Cherie discharged and readmitted to ATU three times due to placement breakdown.	
2014	Intervention • CHC application was successful • CHC approved the request that I continue to provide Dramatherapy for continuity reasons	Aim: support Cherie to manage a successful transition from the ATU to the community.	See Analytical Snapshot: Middle
2015	Review and Intervention Dramatherapist employed by the Arts Therapies Community Team, including an Art Therapist and two Music Therapists with an intergrative approach • Service model: No restrictions time wise • Referral accepted for ongoing Dramatherapy	Cherie living independently in the community Cherie attended ongoing sessions	
2016	Ending process and Evaluation End of intervention negotiated between Cherie and myself • Decision to submit proposal to local health board's annual conference to present together	Cherie asked to share her story Cherie requested Group Dramatherapy	See Analytical Snapshot: End
September 2016	Co-presented at Therapies and Health Science conference. Local. Won best presentation award		
November 2016	Co- presented at the Learning Disabilities Conference: Creative Discoveries. London		
2017 - 2018	Dramatherapy Group	Cherie attended the group	

Figure 11.1 Timeline.

I worked together with Cherie in dramatherapy for over five years. To outline the process leading up to our presenting of her story together, this chapter shares analytical snapshots (Ramsden 2017) of moments from the beginning, middle and end giving context and brief commentary to consider the process.

Analytical Snapshot: Beginning

When we first met, Cherie expressed herself through shouting, screaming, crying and refusing to engage. At times, she thought she did not want to continue living, due to her profound self-hatred and belief that others found her unbearable. During some psychotic episodes, she believed she was pregnant and had given birth to a dead child. Often Cherie was preoccupied with her physical health. It seemed that it was because of Cherie's verbal preoccupation with her physical health, talking therapies had not been successful. Dramatherapy was able to link with the body and work non-verbally, and this holistic, process-based approach met Cherie in a different way.

For many months, I sat on the sofa experiencing her rejection of sessions; she said 'no' every week, apologetically stating she wasn't ready, sometimes screaming at me and sometimes shouting down the corridor. Some of the roles I witnessed were of child, murderous mother, hypochondriac and reactionary: 'rigid in thought and behaviour' (Landy 1993, 213).

Leaning (2013) also shares that his client 'never turned up to any appointments and has never been at home when any psychologist has called on her. We are celebrating this fact. She has made this decision and she is proud of herself' (82). I'm in agreement with how easy it would be for him to collude with the dominant story of a challenging woman, but he chose not to, and, in that way, enabled his client to make choices, choices which were taken away from her in the past.

In time, Cherie chose to work with objects in silence, starting to experience the benefits of aesthetic distance (Jones 2007). She called them 'people' and my invitations to the session became 'to see the people'.

Early in our relationship, Cherie and I were addressing issues of consent – verbally and non-verbally. Embodying this in our relationship, we generated feelings of trust (Chesner 1995) and respect, setting the foundation for enabling choice. We were also beginning to explore the idea of multiple roles using creative methods while remaining in the here and now. Jones (2007, 2010) highlights the power of embodiment. Individuals are able to discover their own physical potential. This helps them communicate more effectively and express themselves through the body. As Chesner states, 'A client may come to experience physical communication as an area of ability and success rather than disability and failure' (Chesner 1995, 47).

Embodying a feeling of holding and of being in control of our therapeutic relationship, allowed Cherie to start exploring her own feelings about her body, body image and how others viewed her body.

Analytical Snapshot: Middle

Having now got to know Cherie well, I offered parts of the story of Disney's (1994) 'The Lion King' to enable Cherie to start exploring some of her grief. Despite her age, I knew she enjoyed Disney films, and it was a safe way for her to explore complex feelings around death. Using toy animals, puppets and fabrics she created 'scarce and empty' the land where Scar is King. In one session, using a hula hoop as an empty water hole, the animals died of thirst, and in another, she declared the toys dead one by one dropping them into a hole. Cherie's relationship with her father was a complex one, and she shared with me her sense of guilt around the relief she felt about his death. The character of Simba's journey to adulthood is tainted by a similar feeling. By using the toys as objects onto which she could project, Cherie indirectly expressed her thoughts and feelings.

We then progressed to working in roles and improvised scenes between 'Harry Potter' and 'Voldemort' in which they were trying to kill one another. Cherie, a Harry Potter fan, started with the characters from the film *Harry Potter and the Philosopher's Stone* (Warner Brothers 2001). Although she knew the film well, she chose to write a script of her own devising, into which she introduced a new character of her own creation called 'The Bogie Man', a ghost who knocked under the table and tried to hurt her by hitting her. He was an imaginary character and we explored different ways of responding to, containing, channelling, accepting and removing the ghost.

In these sessions, Cherie was able to experience playing the role of the villain – the father and the killer. I wondered if the characters of 'Voldemort' and 'The Bogie Man' were metaphors for exploring 'the common sense of death' and 'after death' (Holloway 2012), as well as the feeling of patricide, loss, loss of identity, death itself and the spiritual role, death (Landy 1993).

Working with stories when facing some of the challenges that Cherie presented is well documented (Casson 2004; Dent-Brown 1999; Gersie 1991). In these sessions, we were able to focus therapeutically on imagination, spontaneity, indirect expression and interaction through improvisation, story and role, as Chesner's (1995) 'Dramatherapy Tree' proposes. The Dramatherapy Tree helps to determine the appropriate level of work, when assessing an individual's level of functioning.

Barette and Walmsley (2000) write about death and bereavement in a book co-written and edited by women with learning disabilities. Barette recommends that to help people when their parents die, it is important that they are offered access to the death records, an opportunity to talk to the family solicitor, access to the family home and choose some belongings to keep. In our sessions, Cherie and I were working out together how much she could tolerate being involved. How much responsibility would she like in the future?

Analytical Snapshot: End

In the final months of our time working together, Cherie started of her own accord to be less dependent on the sessions. We established an agreement that she would ring from her mobile phone to let me know if she was choosing not to attend. Sometimes we'd have a long conversation on the phone instead. She said that she wanted to join a group. She hoped I didn't take it personally, but she didn't want to see me on her own and wanted to share with a group of people, who had been through similar experiences. She also admitted she was lonely. During these conversations I often noticed how her internal guide and roles, such as Doctor, Moral Minister and Revolutionary Mother, were emerging.

Cherie told me that 'The Bogie Man' was her father and that he had abused her, and that she was raped by another man. She said her parents had always warned her, imploring she wouldn't be a mother as she couldn't be a good one.

Measuring and Evaluating

As it appeared the sessions were naturally concluding so I offered to review the process with her. We addressed the following topics:

- Cherie's feeling that dramatherapy had helped her change her life, in the following ways:
  - now live independently in my own home, which I have decorated and furnished myself and I've successfully sustained the placement'.
  - only shout and scream sometimes and I know how to get support when I need it'.
  - have good relationships with people'.
  - have choice and control over my health plan, my budgets and an active role in reviewing my care plan'.

- We checked through the CORE LD self-assessment tool, completed pre-, post- and during our sessions, which showed:
  - The overall score was lower, and in particular, Cherie's risk of suicide scored lower as well.
  - In response to the questions about experiencing difficult feelings over the last week, Cherie now chose to respond: 'not at all' or 'sometimes', rather than 'a lot'.

- Qualitative feedback questionnaires:

  Comments from carers and staff's feedback questionnaires: which Cherie later included in the presentation:

  'She is a joy to spend time with, I love being with her'

  'Compared to a few years ago she is a different person, she's done really well'

  'We never have to fill in behaviour reports now, she can tell us how she's feeling, I think that helps'.

- Strategic aims met:
  - Learning Disability Strategy (2017)
  - Prudent Health Care (Guidance: Securing health and well-being for future generations 2016)

These strategic aims are important, as during the period of our work together (2012–2017), the Health Board Trust had begun to draw up a Learning Disability Strategy, which was completed in 2017. The result was an integrated strategy, which had been written in consultation with people with a learning disability, their carers and a range of stakeholders.

As this was of paramount importance within the trust during the decade I worked there, its vision and principles influenced and guided my practice.

It was regularly observed within the MDT that people with learning disabilities were continuously having decisions made for them; therefore, as one of the key areas to be addressed, the first objective of the Strategy was:

> Enabling people to have more control over their lives through Person Centred Planning, Self-Directed Support and Access to Advocacy
> Objective: People with a learning disability will have more choice and control over their life.
>
> (The Mental Health and Learning Disability
> Partnership Board (2012–2017, 8)

To meet this objective, my approach as therapist was to empower the individual to make their own choices, to support them to communicate this choice and to enable it to happen.

Equally, the Prudent Health Care model (Welsh Government 2016) was a move away from dependency, promoting an approach where people and professionals share power and work together in equal partnership. The term 'co-production' was coined in the hope that patients would be more involved in their own care by promoting self-management. Co-production values all participants as equals and is built around people and not around systems.

The Presentation

At some point during our ending evaluation process, Cherie asked if she could share her story.

As we thought about how to create the presentation, a link was made with Casson's theatre model of the 'self as a container'. 'The model provides dramatherapists and psychodramatists with a containing metaphor for the work, combining embodiment, projection and role play in an intrapsychic and interpersonal space which expands the sense of self and empowers the person' (Casson 2004, 162).

We agreed we would have an improvised conversation, but that we needed slides to remind us of important things to address. Cherie was insistent that because of her learning disability, she could not write; so to create a PowerPoint presentation, Cherie dictated and I typed. At times, Cherie typed herself with support and chose the style and images on the screen.

It helped us to visualise the performance theatrically, when thinking about the room and the stage. We thought about the boundaries of 'on and off stage'. Having a sense of where the presentation would take place, offered some predictability, and we physically set out the space with furniture in our rehearsal room. We also arranged that there would be a run-through with some of the people organising the conference.

We began by breaking down the details of the presentation in terms of their theatrical function, as suggested by Casson:

- **Roles:** We could be frankly explicit that we were co-producing and both taking on storyteller roles. 'Every part of the theatre has different roles implicit in it. Creating and playing these roles offers opportunities for self-exploration, expression and expansion' (Casson 2004, 158). Cherie was being a writer, designer, director, producer and performer.
- **Stage curtain:** Casson says 'In effect, the person is in charge of when this revelatory act occurs' (Casson 2004, 158). This metaphorical curtain offered in symbolic terms that Cherie was indeed in charge of how much and what she revealed.
- **Scenery:** We knew we would have a microphone, so we rehearsed with a prop. The PowerPoint presentation was to be projected behind us, so Cherie chose some of her artwork to be photographed to appear on screen.
- **On stage:** We decided how we were to be on stage together, and how much I was required to do, so that Cherie was enabled and empowered to do as much as she chose to.
- **The action:** Cherie wanted people to see and hear her use her voice, to show how much she had changed and how dramatherapy had helped her.
- **Backstage:** I took this to imply the therapeutic system we were working in. We should review issues of consent and check what we were doing wasn't abusive. For myself, this meant not only referring to supervision but also feeding back to the monthly MDT meeting. We wanted our process to be transparent.
- **After the performance:** Casson offers questions such as who is in the audience? and what does the critic write? We also thought about what changes we as directors might make. This ongoing reflective process of review allowed the process to be creative and fluid.
- **Closure:** An attention to feelings at the end, to be compassionate and to reflect.

One of Cherie's aims in doing the presentation was to help others. Cherie's most protective factor was her kindness and ability to care for others. In this process, we started to work more directly 'psycho-educationally' (Gilbert 2013), talking about recognition (Chesner 1995) and cultivating a compassionate mind. Within *Compassion Focused Therapy* (Gilbert 2013), there is a focus on learning about the evolution of the brain, described as 'old brain, new brain'. Gilbert propounds an integration of ideas concerning: Jungian archetypes, evolutionary approaches to human behaviour, neuroscientific and cognitive-behavioural ideas about the way that people think and behave and Buddhist philosophy concerning compassion and mindfulness. We spoke about this theory and applied it to Cherie's experience.

Clapton et al. (2018) have written about adapting *Compassion Focused Therapy for people with Intellectual Disabilities* (CFT-ID), and how this approach can bring a positive change. CFT-ID identifies three systems: a soothing system, a drive system and a threat system. Working in the body, Dramatherapy is a perfect way of mobilising these three systems, and our presentation was an example of how we could bring the three systems into 'the action' (Casson 2004).

> The theatre of the self includes working with the body…Dramatherapists… work with the body encouraging breathing, movement, expression and play.
>
> (Casson 2004, 159).

Together we created a compassionate kitbag of soothing ideas, images and stories from our sessions, which Cherie collected and photographed for the presentation. Gilbert states that those from shaming backgrounds are very unclear about what self-compassion is. 'They may be caring of other people or able to defend themselves or focused on "achieving" things or winning social approval – but genuine care and concern for their own well-being is different' (Gilbert 2013, 220). We learnt that Cherie's belief had long been that you should always put others first; however, we had now developed her sense of compassion towards herself.

Cherie had already experienced, before I met her, many of the roles that she displayed in producing and performing the presentation; she has always been a mother, a survivor, a helper and a storyteller. At times, she had to take on other roles in order to survive, sometimes shutting off feelings and sometimes shutting out the objective world.

> One plays roles, then, primarily to get in and out of oneself and to master both that which is situated inside, the role taken, and outside, the objective world. The more competently one plays out one's roles, the more one will develop an ease in navigating the sometimes-difficult boundaries between internal and external experience.
>
> (Landy 1993, 40)

During the presentations, Cherie demonstrated how competent she had become in navigating her own experience of herself.

Context, Culture and Models of Working

Within the culture I was working in, it wasn't easy to remain open and compassionate, but working in a reflective team helped. Barnaby & Sharma (2016) have written about the benefits of working collaboratively. As behaviour therapist and dramatherapist, applying behaviour analysis (ABA) and positive behavioural support (PBS) as a means of meeting goals, MDT working proved valuable in enhancing social relationships and interpersonal communication.

Following a period of assessment, the dramatherapist's data was made available to 'formulation meetings', where staff considered all the information that had been gathered about Cherie. It enabled the team to have a conversation and to examine their different perspectives. We used a model called *Team Formulation* (Lake 2008) which considers staff feelings and transference, responses of others and repeated relationship patterns. Within this behavioural model, we could acknowledge emotions, bring in developmental history and provide a systemic approach. It is a co-constructed circular model, so when different professionals suggested their hypotheses (thoughts and ideas about the individual's presentation), the conversation between us could lead to new understanding. This allowed us to follow more of the social model of disability (Chappell et al. 2001), while keeping the individual's needs at the centre of treatment delivery. By being based firmly in psychological services, the arts therapists could be supported to sustain reflective practice and stay compassionate. Hill and Harding's (2019) chapter outlines their approach and the culture they tried to create, explaining the benefits of formulation. Working in a culture where hypotheses are not fixed enables freedom rather than a stuckness and offers an opportunity and confidence to act on new ideas.

> It relates to the concept that hypotheses are just ideas about what is happening between people. It's breaking that ice, just doing it, and it helps me to not get married to a particular idea (hypothesis). I think it's important to generate lots of hypotheses to maintain openness.
>
> (Hill and Harding 2019, 136)

Nevertheless, there was a resistance to working reflectively when individuals presented with behaviour as challenging as in Cherie's case. The traditional medical model had strong roots in the service, and no doubt influenced attitudes and beliefs within the MDT.

> The medical model of disability adopts a deficit approach and places the cause of disability on the individual who cannot function 'normally' because of their impairments, namely physical, psychological or cognitive difference. Therefore, the solution to the 'problem' of disability is to change the individual, and the expert in this case is a professional of some kind.
>
> (Reeve 2019, 38)

Another contribution to this resistance was that the institutionalised culture meant the team often felt that change was impossible. I often noticed that the counter transference was a disempowerment and impotence around the capacity to think. Dramatherapist Gardner-Hynd writes about this and the importance of understanding this culture as a mirror of society and the system's attitude towards people with learning disabilities, which 'devalue individuals with learning disabilities and see them as incapable, or not of value, rather than as active agents in their own lives' (Gardner-Hynd 2010, 176).

Cherie had first-hand experience of this attitude. Cherie was clear that she wanted to educate others into realising that the health services need to develop better ways to support people with learning disabilities, and that she had ideas about how to do this. She felt it important to share her findings with a wider audience. It was this request that led us to perform our presentation again at a national learning disabilities conference in London. At this event, there were not many people with learning disabilities presenting, although they were in attendance, and during a conversation with the organisers, Cherie asked why this was. During this evaluation process, while Cherie's aims were not always explicit, her involvement led to a greater awareness for herself and others.

Reflections on Co-Producing an Evaluation

A 2013 research project by people with learning disabilities (Northway et al. 2013) alluded to the benefits of greater awareness, claiming that the benefits of inclusivity and active participation are to be expected, but there are wider benefits also of interest. By using the term 'participatory research', this project was an example of how people with learning disabilities could be a co-researcher; one of the aims of which was to disseminate the findings. The study concluded that:

> people with learning disabilities have a valuable role to play in developing, undertaking and disseminating research.
>
> (Northway et al. 2013, 6)

'For the co-researchers one of the most frequent observations was how they felt they had increased their self-confidence [...and] were described by those listening as being "professional" and "inspirational"' (Northway et al. 2013, 64). Cherie received similar feedback from members in the audience following our presentations.

It was this confidence and her experience of positive feedback which enabled Cherie to tolerate group therapy, where she encouraged other group members by offering them similar praise. She also encouraged other group members to tell their stories, reassuring them that it was safe and empowering to do so.

As well as thinking about the benefits, the co-researchers' second learning point was that the process of sharing the stories about abuse can be distressing, so support should be provided during the process. Importantly, they state that to *not* undertake such research, would mean that the voices of people with learning disabilities remain unheard and their experiences not addressed (Northway et al. 2013, 64).

I would argue that as dramatherapists, we have the skills to deal with this dilemma, offering a safe stage for the difficult experiences to be heard. In their 2011 article, Ramsden and Jones discuss the subtle methods of communication that children used to express their consent during their research project, such as nodding and shaking heads, raising shoulders and eyebrows and using words and phrases. They concluded that, as well as ensuring an individualised approach for each participant, 'the researcher/therapist must be significantly experienced in understanding the processes of listening, reflecting and engaging in actions derived from such communications' (Ramsden & Jones 2011, 192). They agree that being aware of potential abusive practices is essential in this process.

> Complex issues such as understanding and meaning making, voluntariness, influence, bias, power, control and environment must be taken into account, including psychological considerations [...] This potential could, for example, be expressed in a need to please the researcher or, conversely, a need to act out as a healthy expression of a disempowered life situation.
>
> (Ramsden & Jones 2011, 184)

However, at a conference in 2017, when talking about how this project had empowered children, Jones was emphatic that to *not* involve them is to silence them, and thus 'their stories remain, distant and strange or unheard, so that opinions and experiences are not given value' (Jones 2017).

Conclusion

As dramatherapists, we can use our own working model, stay compassionate and be aware of the complexities of verbal and non-verbal communication around consent and challenging feelings. It is possible to empower people to tell the story of their own experience of dramatherapy and to involve them in the evaluation process.

It is imperative to note that Cherie did not get rewarded financially for co-presenting. The 2013 research project by people with learning disabilities (Northway et al. 2013) recommends that, in future participatory research, careful attention should be given as to how people with learning disabilities can be employed for more hours. This is certainly something I would endorse.

Equally, our conference presentations were not public performances; the audiences were allied health professionals and arts therapists, who have an understanding of themselves of the benefits of co-production. To extend a method of evaluation such as this would need careful consideration of the impact on the audiences and on the individual sharing their story through a presentation, 'to avoid burdening those who risk performing their stories with increased cultural stigmatisation' (Sajnani 2010, 190).

Cherie spoke candidly about the different people she had met while co-presenting, and the access it had given her to a wider world, very different to the world she had been living in. During our closing reflection on the presentation process, Cherie said that playing with all the 'people' and talking on the stage made her arrive at the realisation: 'I want to be me'.

As Landy says, 'The need to play roles comes from one's need to assert oneself in the world' (Landy 1993, 39), and every individual deserves the chance to meet this need, if they chose to.

References

Barette, P. & Walmsley, J. 2000. 'Death and bereavement'. In: Atkinson, D., McCarthy, M., Walmsley, J., Cooper, M., Rolph, S., Aspis, S., Barette, P., Coventry, M., & Ferris, G. eds. *Good Times, Bad Times: Women with Learning Difficulties Telling Their Stories.* Birmingham: BILD Publications.

Barnaby, R. & Sharma, N. 2016. 'Working collaboratively in a multi-professional team'. In: Miller, C. ed. *Arts Therapists in Multidiscipliary Settings Working Together for Better Outcomes*, 95–108. London: Jessica Kingsley Publishers.

Casson, J. 2004. *Drama, Psychotherapy and Psychosis Dramatherapy and Psychodrama with People Who Hear Voices.* Hove: Brunner-Routledge.

Chappell, A.L., Goodley, D. & Lawthom, R. 2001. 'Making connections: The relevance of the social model of disability for people with learning difficulties'. In: *British Journal of Learning Disabilities*, 9(2), 45–50. Wiley Online Library.

Chesner, A. 1995. *Dramatherapy for People with Learning Disabilities: A World of Difference.* London: Jessica Kingsley Publishers.

Clapton, N.E., Williams, J., Griffith, G., & Jones, R.S. 2018. 'Finding the person you really are … on the inside: Compassion focused therapy for adults with intellectual disabilities'. In: *Journal of Intellectual Disabilities,* 22, 135–153. London: Sage.

Dent-Brown, K. 1999. 'The six part story method (6PSM) as an aid in the assessment of personality disorder'. In: *Dramatherapy,* 21(2), 10–14. London: Routledge.

Disney. 1994. *The Lion King.* [DVD] Directed by Minkoff, R. & Allers, R. Burbank, CA: Walt Disney Feature Animation.

Gardner-Hynd, N. 2010. 'Learning disabilities and acute mental health'. In: Jones, P. ed. *Drama as Therapy Volume 2: Clinical Work and Research into Practice,* 172–188. London: Routledge.

Gersie, A. 1991. *Storymaking in Bereavement.* London: Jessica Kingsley.

Gilbert, P. 2013. *The Compassionate Mind.* London: Constable.

Hill, C. & Harding, C. 2019. 'Working systemically with multidisciplinary teams'. In: Jones & Haydon –Laurelut. eds. *Working with People with Learning Disabilities. Systemic Approaches,* 132–149. London: Red Globe Press.

Holloway, P. 2012. 'Surviving suicide: The book of life and death'. In: Dokter, D., Holloway, P., & Seebohm, H. eds. *Dramatherapy and Destructiveness,* 157–176. London: Routledge.

Jones, P. 2007. *Drama as Therapy, Theory, Practice and Research.* London: Routledge.

Jones, P. 2010. *Drama as Therapy Volume 2: Clinical Work and Research into Practice.* London: Routledge.

Jones, P. 2017. "Silencing and voice: Ways of rethinking the arts, participation and research". *From the Inside: Shining a Light on the Collaborative Process between Therapist and Client Dramatherapy Wales Conference*, Cwmbran, 17 November.

Lake, N. 2008. 'Developing skills in team consultation 2: A team formulation approach'. *Clinical Psychology Forum*, 186, 18–24.

Landy, R.J. 1993. *Persona and Performance The Meaning of Role in Drama, Therapy and Everyday Life*. London: Jessica Kingsley Publishers.

Leaning, B. 2013. 'The funnel: A brief narrative'. In *Clinical Psychology & People with Learning Disabilities*, 11(1 and 2). The British Psychological Society. Accessed: https://explore.bps.org.uk/content/bpsfpid/11/1-2/82 and the British Psychologial Society references a DOI: https://doi.org/10.53841/bpsfpid.2013.11.1–2.82.

Northway, R., Melsome, M., Flood, S., Bennett, D., Howarth, J. & Thomas, B. 2013. 'How do people with intellectual disabilities view abuse and abusers?'. In: *Journal of Intellectual Disabilities*, 17(4), 361–375. London: SAGE.

Ramsden, E. 2017. 'Supporting agency, choice making and the expression of 'voice' with Kate: Dramatherapy in a mainstream primary school setting with a 9-year-old girl diagnosed with ASD and ADHD'. In: Haythorne, D. & Seymour, A. eds. *Dramatherapy and Autism*, 53–65. Routledge.

Ramsden, E. & Jones, P. 2011. 'Ethics, children, education and therapy: Vulnerable or empowered'. In Campbell, A. & Broadhead, P. eds. *Working with Children and Young People: Ethical Debates and Practices across Disciplines and Continents*, 179–196 Germany: Peter Lang.

Reeve, D. 2019. 'Understanding disabling barriers faced by people with learning difficulties: The social model and beyond'. In: Jones & Haydon-Laurelut Eds. *Working with People with Learning Disabilites. Systemic Approaches*, 36–50. London: Red Globe Press.

Sajnani, N. 2010. 'Mind the Gap: Facilitating transformative witnessing amongst audiences'. In: Jones, P. ed. *Drama as Therapy Volume 2: Clinical Work and Research into Practice*, 189–207. London: Routledge.

The Mental Health and Learning Disability Partnership Board. 2012–2017. *A Strategy for People with a Learning Disability* [online] Available at: https://abuhb.nhs.wales/ (Accessed September 2020).

Warner Brothers. 2001. *Harry Potter and the Philosopher's Stone*. [DVD] Directed by C. Columbus. Watford, Hertfordshire and Burbank, CA: Warner Bros Pictures.

Welsh Government. (last updated February 2016) *Securing health and well-being for future generations* [online] Available at https://gov.wales/sites/default/files/publications/2019-04/securing-health-and-well-being-for-future-generations.pdf (Accessed September 2020).

Chapter 12

Roots to Grow

The Development of Dramatherapy in a Low-Secure Service for Men with Learning Disabilities

Jennifer Pullan

The following chapter describes the establishment of a dramatherapy service within a low-secure hospital, which specialises in learning disabilities and/or autism for male clients within the UK National Health Service (NHS). Clients are detained under the Mental Health Act (1983) and present with a history of offending behaviour and/or high-risk behaviours, which place them and others at risk. Experiences will be drawn upon from my work as a newly appointed dramatherapist in a setting where no qualified arts psychotherapies had previously been provided. This will be illustrated by clinical vignettes of individual dramatherapy with Jack, a client with a learning disability, who may or may not also be on the autistic spectrum. A large number of clients admitted to this service are often found to sit on the spectrum alongside their learning disability.

This chapter respects and remarks upon the unhelpful labels placed upon this client group, highlighting key aspects of Jack's development and growth while engaging in dramatherapy. Description of a shared creative language, interpersonal experiences and emphasis on trauma will be outlined. The frequent themes of patience, time, repetition and resistance will also come to light, as consistent with forensic services and learning disabilities.

The Service

Within this low-secure service, which covers two inpatient wards and one rehabilitation ward, dramatherapy remains, at the time of writing, the only arts therapies provision. It was introduced on a permanent basis in 2018. Before this, the service had little experience and knowledge of the arts psychotherapies. This required introductory workshops with experiential components, in order to aid the staff teams to understand the nature of dramatherapy and how it may work. Parallel to this, ran the learning needs of the clients themselves who had very little, if any, experience of the arts psychotherapies. Many dramatherapists and indeed fellow arts therapists often find themselves in this position; we are fortunate that it is built into our training to develop autonomy, remain resilient, strong and tenacious in the ways and means of integrating into services. A recently qualified therapist may enter into a new role believing the challenge lies mainly in educating the client group.

DOI: 10.4324/9781003091783-16

However, it may come as no surprise that the biggest barrier is often between the therapist and fellow colleagues, who, unconsciously, hold great influence over the clients' perceptions of therapy. Stokes describes each profession holding differing 'emotional motivations', and using Bion's 'basic assumption mentality' (Stokes 1994, 162), he rightly stresses the importance of collaboration among the team towards shared goals. In the service, we focus upon here, the client's voice is often heard as a part of the team, usually with support from an external advocate.

There can be potentially negative expectations regarding working with people with learning disabilities: preconceived notions about concrete thinking, perseverative behaviour and disinclination to change. Often, I was, and still am, met with surprising and usually pleasant interactions, whereby clients with learning disabilities are open to trying 'new things', which, in the case of dramatherapy, is inspiring, as we continually find innovative ways of working. As well as the volatile nature of working in a forensic setting, continually shifting risk, unpredictable behaviours and alternating support staff, the nature of this client group is often embroiled in childhood trauma, disrupted upbringing with associated attachment difficulties, and challenges with social integration. The clients in this service have been admitted under section through the criminal justice system (further information regarding sections can be found under the Mental Health Act 1983). Some men have carried out an offence leading to conviction or, in some cases, awaiting trial but are deemed too vulnerable to sit on remand in the prison services. Other clients may have been admitted because they present with highly risky behaviours and are referred from secondary care community teams.

Most of the clients remain in this service for a minimum of two years, usually transitioning through the acute to sub-acute wards and to on-site rehabilitation. A national plan proposed by NHS England in 2015 has led to the development of *Transforming Care* (Houlden 2015), a strategy which proposes a push towards the development of community services and reduction of hospital admissions, specifically for people with a learning disability and/or autism, who are also experiencing difficulties with mental health. Despite the *Transforming Care* agenda, clients can often remain in the service for a substantial amount of time, while the supporting team strives to find a suitable placement (an environment in which the client can live with as much independence as permitted by safe-guarding restrictions). Placements all seek to keep both the client and the public safe.

Offending behaviours within this client group are often associated with sexual offences (frequently against children), arson and aggression. These behaviours usually stem from the long-term effects of disturbed backgrounds. Developmental milestones through childhood have often been missed, and these clients may have experienced severe systemic abuse and unease; they 'often lack social skills and have problems identifying and connecting with emotions. They show an unfamiliarity with listening to and being thought about by others', in turn impacting their emotional development (O'Connell & Montague 2016).

Often clients have been placed into care as children, moving from place to place with no firm abode to call 'home'. They may have been subjected to bullying due to their learning disability or victimised within the family unit for the very same reason. These disturbances in a person's upbringing have an impact on their mental health and, furthermore, increase their chance of offending (Sinason 1997). Entwined with this is the struggle with their learning disability and a striving to find their identity and place within a rather large and terrifying world. In dramatherapy, we can begin work with these men who are still trying to find their identity and discover a sense of self.

There is little evidence-based literature on dramatherapy with forensic clients holding dual diagnoses of mental illness and learning disabilities. This, perhaps, enables us to understand why there are so few dramatherapists commissioned to work in these sectors and why it is important to develop this area of research. However, there are changes; in late 2019, NHS England issued a call for submissions, in which arts therapists were given a platform to present their work, evidencing its impact and benefit on the services in which we are working.

In line with innovative approaches and the need to provide varying methods of treatment, the low-secure service, discussed in this chapter, opened its doors to dramatherapy. Being a newly appointed clinician in a well-established team and service, has its advantages and disadvantages, just as for a client entering a service for the first time. Advantages of the clinician may be a fresh perspective, new creative approaches to the work and the 'eagerness' that can often be attributed to newly qualified therapists. Similar themes have been identified in the clients themselves, as they move through services and arrive in new and possibly daunting places. Our clients with learning disabilities may be subjected to over-stimulating environments as they move through the criminal justice system, often with a desire to 'fit in' and continually searching for ways to connect with others. This is a client group regularly ostracised, not only due to their learning disability, but now, alongside it, a criminal conviction. These clients (as with dramatherapy) are frequently misunderstood across society and have difficulties in finding a voice and pushing for it to be heard in a healthy manner. Perhaps, for clients failing to be heard, their main method of communication is through fire setting, violence or abusive acts.

A Shared Creative Language

The clinician must be constantly observant of individual behavioural responses, as these behaviours, however apparently bizarre, may be demonstrating the way in which the patient finds it most acceptable to communicate (Boardman et al 2014).

Often, when working with clients with learning disabilities, communication can be perceived as a barrier and invariably results in what is deemed 'challenging behaviour', as the client is unable to express needs in a way which the neuro-typical person may understand. The question is 'who does this behaviour challenge?' When labelling clients with this term, it may be with reference to the impact on caregivers and supporting network – but is consideration given to the challenge the client themself is facing, trying to be heard and find a voice which others might understand?

While highlighting the importance of clients having a voice, Chesner (1995) alludes to the difficulties clients with learning disabilities may experience with expressing themselves. Dramatherapy utilises gesture, eye contact, body language, and silences, with less emphasis on the spoken word or the client's cognitive expression of feelings within the space. It is, in part, down to the role of the therapist to take on the responsibility of formulating the unspoken transactions taking place within the encounter.

In a clinical setting, it is important to find a mutual understanding and shared language not only within the therapeutic relationship but between ourselves as clinicians. Frequently within multidisciplinary team (MDT) discussions, psychologically informed clinicians find themselves communicating *on behalf* of the client, navigating through medicalised terminology in order to enhance the team's understanding of the client's internal world.

In dramatherapy, the opportunities to communicate creatively are endless and can provide offenders with learning disabilities the chance to explore their own preferred methods of communicating. For a client group, who has generally struggled to have their needs heard and met, which in turn impacts emotional maturity and developmental progression, the chance to access channels of communication, to enable their voices to be heard, is crucial to healing and growth. The use of creativity within dramatherapy enables a sense of play, which allows for a trusting therapeutic relationship to form. When working with clients who have experienced trauma, it may take a long period of time and gentle, playful interventions for the client to feel safe and secure.

A number of clients show a desire to engage creatively and often express interest in decorating and using masks within sessions. The use of masks within forensic settings is not uncommon, as offenders may have an unconscious desire to remain 'hidden'. Through mask work, they are able to express this need and approach the self that lies underneath, in a safe and creative manner. 'The therapeutic masquerade aims to unmask the self through masking a part of the self that has been repressed' (Landy 1985). Often, the part that remains hidden is ridden with guilt, shame and pain, whether in relation to the index offence explicitly or connected to traumatic early experiences. However, one may argue that there lies no separation here, and the shame tied to forensic risk is linked just as strongly to childhood trauma. The clinical formulation, which outlines an understanding of the client's internal world, often presents a complex network linking current risky behaviours with early experiences and a perpetual cycle of anger, usually attributed to shame and pain.

Through the use of masks, clients have the opportunity to cover parts of the self they wish to remain hidden; however, within dramatherapy, we can discover not only what the mask conceals but also may be what it represents. The choice to use masks within sessions may on the surface indicate a desire to be creative and explore new techniques, as was the case with Jack.

VIGNETTE 1   Jack

Jack would often show apprehension about the creative work, a discomfort and reluctance to play. While walking towards a session with another client, I passed Jack on the ward. He noticed the blank mask I held in my hand. Jack showed interest in the mask, then requested he 'do something' with masks in his own dramatherapy sessions. This was then offered. Jack had been working with a story he recalled from childhood: Goldilocks and the Three Bears. His request to use masks provided a stepping stone into working with this story in more depth.

Jack spent a number of sessions decorating/designing each character. He chose the young bear's face to work on first, which subsequently ended up being the one character which resonated with him the most. It appeared as though the young bear provided a sense of comfort as he embarked upon this creative way of working.

Jack was a man in his 20s with a learning disability, who attended individual dramatherapy for 14 months. He would adopt a friendly persona, likeable and with minimal incidents recorded while on the wards. This contradicted the severity of his index offence and would often lead me to question his 'true' nature. How could a man of such friendly and seemingly genuine demeanour have been involved with a seriously violent act?

There appeared from under the surface not only a dangerous and unpredictable element to his personality but also a young man so vulnerable to others and to the environments he finds himself in.

The dramatherapy referral outlined a need for the team to get to know more about him. It was difficult to determine who Jack really was and thus to develop a reliable formulation. He depicted a desire to 'mask' himself and prevent others from knowing the 'real' him. As with many clients with learning disabilities, it is probable Jack was unsure of who he was himself; his self-identity made up of damaging and abusive words heard throughout his years, internalised and fixed into his own belief system.

Imagine having repeatedly experienced persecutory comments at a young age, an age at which we hope to develop a healthy sense of self. Imagine the possibility of constant upheaval, broken attachments and lack of steady support figures. Compared to a neuro-typical population, young children with learning disabilities are more likely to find themselves in toxic living situations as the caregivers may have difficulties communicating and understanding the needs of the child. Both struggle and, without support and guidance, both may feel they are falling and failing. If the child continues without support and is not provided with an understanding of their own learning disability, how can they then develop a stable understanding of who they are? Their emotional growth is stunted, as inadequate support is provided. A child desperately trying to understand and find their own place in the world, perhaps an abusive and harmful world, then believes that to find a way to belong, they must themselves engage in harmful acts, as they may have witnessed and been subjected to. It is down this path, we can begin to identify how a young child with learning disabilities has journeyed towards offending behaviour.

It is only right that we then provide these clients and their inner child with the support and nurturing which may have been absent during developmental years. By accessing material rooted in early experiences, through creativity and a shared language, such as that of the story of Goldilocks and the Three Bears, we can promote emotional maturity and a chance to support clients in understanding their own emotions through the eyes of their chosen characters, through the metaphor.

VIGNETTE 2   Goldilocks and the Three Bears

Jack continued to work with the character of the young bear throughout sessions, choosing this character above others. With gentle encouragement, he created the 'faces' of and further explored the remaining three characters. Jack developed the story through the eyes of the characters, wearing the masks and answering questions he himself had suggested.

The story developed into a macabre, murderous one as he described the death of Goldilocks's parents, and these deaths being kept secret from the child. The theme of secrecy continued throughout the story and mirrored my own understanding (or lack of) regarding Jack himself. What was being kept secret? What was being hidden? Why was he choosing to mask parts of himself?

I found myself eager to find out more and 'unmask' the secrecy. There developed a desire to uncover and discover who Jack was and why. However, it was crucial to remember that this was a gradual and gentle process whereby Jack required time, repetition, frequent reminders of previous sessions and their content, plus a tentative approach, in order to support him in gathering what he needed from the process as opposed to what I felt and what the team 'needed'.

As a therapist developing a service within a service, it can become easy and somewhat dangerous to collude with systemic needs such as 'quick discharge' and limiting admission time. Recognising a desire to meet the objectives and wishes of the team and institution, as opposed to the client's needs, can create barriers within the therapeutic journey. It is probable that within the counter-transference, the client's process will be tainted by the wider 'needs', if the therapist is not careful in managing these 'objectives' effectively. The therapist's role is to journey alongside the client at their pace, while simultaneously working as a part of the team and holding goals in mind. However, in developing and establishing a new dramatherapy service, there is a danger in wanting to 'please' and show how 'well' the modality can work, losing focus of the clients' individual needs and growth.

This may sound familiar, in that clients with learning disabilities may also strive to feel a sense of purpose and justify their existence. A parallel process takes place, whereby this new and unfamiliar treatment modality tries to find its position in the wider service. The individual (therapist or client) endeavours to build and establish identity. Jack continued to find a sense of *him*self through the clinical work.

VIGNETTE 3   Growing through Role-Play

Having started his character work with the youngest bear, Jack then progressed through the family, as though he himself was growing in age and developing alongside the characters he chose to role-play with masks.

As Jack's creative repertoire began to progress through the sessions, his development of characters mirrored his insight into his own narrative and desire to talk and share personal experiences. Initially, Jack had shown avoidance towards discussing his index offence; however, over time, he expressed a desire to explore this directly within his individual psychology sessions, which focussed upon offending behaviours. In dramatherapy, he would share childhood memories and family dynamics.

During the first year of dramatherapy, Jack would fill in circles provided on a template sheet using coloured pens, as a check-in and check-out. Towards the end of his dramatherapy journey, he would choose not to complete these circles and would instead use verbal means to communicate his thoughts and feelings, as though able to express himself with greater ease and understanding.

As Jack progressed through the story and characters, he appeared to internalise the work, which led to his own growth, understanding of self and enabled him to develop emotional integrity.

In the story of Goldilocks and the Three Bears, there begins an unfolding process whereby Goldilocks shows a desire to find her place. She moves from bowl to bowl, chair to chair, bed to bed, to find somewhere she feels comfortable, to find a sense of belonging. Prompted by the story, Jack began to refer to dynamics within his own family unit. It appeared as though moments within the story and experiences the characters describe, reminded him of his personal narrative. Due to Jack's learning disability, it could be challenging for him to find these connections when asked within sessions. This would be an abstract concept to him, and consciously connecting the story to himself would cause him confusion and difficulty in answering my questions. As he himself was navigating through the dramatherapy process, I would also be finding my way and searching for a path which he could clearly see and walk along with guidance. Jack required plenty of repetition session to session to aid his memory and consolidate the experiences occurring within the therapeutic process. Dramatherapy opened opportunities to build trust and communicate on an unconscious level.

Holding the session weekly, providing consistency and familiarity, aided Jack in feeling a sense of safety. The repeated check-in and check-out, often through drawing and the use of projection, ensured containment. While providing dramatherapy in a forensic setting for clients with a learning disability, the consistent approaches and use of familiar techniques are paramount. Chesner (1995) describes the importance of a 'regular structure for containment', which will help build a sense of trust within the therapeutic relationship. This is a concept often lost among this client group as they have rarely experienced genuine, trustworthy relationships: instead, they have often experienced trauma. These nuances, consistency, check-in and check-out and a folder for the client to hold their work and to access within the session, all create a shared language by which trust and rapport are developed. These actions are symbolic; a form of communication by which the client can understand they are safe and being held.

Trauma

Within the NHS, trauma-informed approaches are being sought and increasingly spoken of. There is recognition of the impact trauma has on interpersonal experiences, and a drive towards staff engaging with clients in a meaningful and sensitive manner, promoting a culture of choice, empowerment, safety, collaboration and trust (Harris & Fallot 2001). These trauma-informed principles unite with core values held by the arts therapies. These developments taking place within the NHS bring an element of hope for both arts therapists and more importantly the clients.

The work of dramatherapy with male offenders allows insight into their internal world, aiding the client to build their own understanding of the self. Through this and by accessing childhood memories in a safe and distanced (Landy 1983) manner, the client has the opportunity to re-process underlying trauma which contributes towards their offending behaviours. The aim of forensic services is to reduce recidivism (likelihood of re-offending). Therefore, providing a trauma-informed approach such as dramatherapy enables clients to access suppressed memories and gain understanding of their offending behaviours, which in turn supports them in developing a greater amount of control over their responses and attributed behaviours.

The clinical vignettes show how Jack made use of a story which connected to his own narrative. Through the mask work, role-play and creative interactions, both the therapist and Jack could begin to uncover important themes and describe a darkness which, at first, he felt uncomfortable exploring. While working alongside offenders with learning disabilities, to outwardly encourage the use of imagination can inhibit the client's process and cause confusion, as we use abstract thinking. As this service has developed, it has revealed that clients truly do have the ability to engage an active imagination and, in time, can connect abstract thought to conscious understanding. The key word here is 'time', and I would add in 'patience' and 'compassion'. Meeting systemic demands (by this, I mean the immediate team, commissioners, ministry of justice) and colluding with the desire to rehabilitate and 'fix' clients can lead to time pressures and the constant need to provide evidence of recovery. However, trauma-informed clinicians know that while working with such fragile states of being, the journey of recovery and healing cannot be rushed.

Dramatherapy is built on trust between the client and the therapist. To uncover and work with trauma requires strength in trust and rapport, as the client will not access their trauma unless they feel they have a space in which to do so safely. By constructing a shared language within the creative space, whether through the use of story, drawing and/or games, trust builds gradually and takes time and patience. A playful environment allows a means of expression (Sajnani et al 2014). While working with adult male offenders, the concept of play and creativity can be perceived as 'childish'. This can be seen as a barrier which requires restructuring and working through with both the client and the institution. An added element to this is the client's resistance towards feeling like a child. By this, I do not mean feeling intimidated and patronised (which clients in this setting have expressed from time to time) but the feeling of vulnerability. For clients who use aggressive tendencies such as violence, fire setting or rape, the acknowledgement of being a vulnerable person themselves is met with defensiveness and anger. Within forensics, I have found that a rich session in which a client begins to access trauma and their feelings of vulnerability can in turn lead to disengagement, distance and refusal to attend the subsequent session(s). There may have been a moment of connection and shared insight, the client feels 'seen'. As we start to unpick the metaphor used within sessions, clients begin to connect and find meaning within this shared creative realm, which can be like the opening of Pandora's box. This being 'seen' is challenging for the client, and they might try to disconnect themselves from the therapeutic journey.

The therapist is left feeling abandoned, confused and with a sense of 'what did I do wrong?' The projective identification portrayed in these encounters reflects a psychic process, which often surfaces within forensics and, in particular, forensics and learning disabilities. By the therapist continuing to offer the weekly space, despite the client's resistance and refusal, a sense of hope is held and eventually internalised by the client, who feels they may be able to return to the space and enter back into a trusted encounter. This aids in rebuilding healthy attachments and promotes emotional growth and development. Clients usually show resistance in accessing trauma; however, through the creative medium, we can begin to encourage acknowledgement of the pain that may have been caused by childhood difficulties but which have been carried through to adult life.

For Jack, it seemed he had begun to find a means of expression which allowed him to access the darker and more hidden parts of himself. A deterioration in Jack's physical health during the wider global pandemic, followed by the therapist taking a period of leave, meant the sessions were discontinued. However, it was clear that Jack had started to 'unmask' himself and trusted in the therapeutic space where he could begin to develop an understanding of his emotions, thus allowing access into exploration of the index offence. This may in turn have supported his choice to enter into offence-based treatment. McAlister describes dramatherapy as 'an area where playing and creativity can lead to insight and remorse, and paradoxically a greater awareness of risk and destructiveness' (2011). It is hoped that Jack himself felt able to continue this work within his individual psychology sessions.

Conclusion

This chapter has set out to highlight the importance and necessity of holding the following prominent themes in mind, when providing dramatherapy within a forensic low-secure service for men with learning disabilities.

- Patience
- Time
- Repetition
- Resistance

These four key themes are relevant not only to arts psychotherapies but arguably to the wider MDT and ward staff. By respecting these and using a trauma-informed approach (in which these four are of importance), an accessible and strong encounter may be developed. The varied approach and flexibility of dramatherapy provides an accessible form of treatment which can be tailored to the needs of individuals with learning disabilities. Providing a creative form of psychological therapy falls in line with trauma-informed approaches which health-care sectors are seeking to develop.

This chapter has highlighted the benefits of dramatherapy in working with clients, who otherwise may have struggled to engage in treatment – clients labelled with the aforementioned 'challenging behaviour'. These clients have been given an opportunity to develop an emotional repertoire and a sense of self, while the dramatherapy service itself has followed a similar path. Just as clients may learn, develop and grow through the therapy, so dramatherapy itself also learns to develop and grow alongside the clients.

As dramatherapists, we have a special opportunity not just to develop a service to offer clients but to allow those clients to aid our services to become rooted and established. This becomes a joint journey to find support, validation and an opportunity to take steps towards development and growth.

References

Boardman, L., Bernal, J. & Hollins, S. 2014. 'Communicating with people with intellectual disabilities: a guide for general psychiatrists'. In: *Advances in Psychiatric Treatment*, 20(1) pp. 27–36. Cambridge University Press.

Chesner, A. 1995. *Dramatherapy for People with Learning Disabilities a World of Difference*. London: Jessica Kingsley Publishers.

Harris, M. & Fallot, E. eds. 2001. *Using Trauma Theory to Design Service Systems. New Directions for Mental Health Services*. San Francisco, CA: Jossey-Bass. (Sourced from): https://people.nhs.uk/guides/conversations-about-painful-subjects/steps/talking-about-trauma/ (Accessed 13 April 2021).

Houlden, A. 2015. *Building the Right Support*. Available at: https://www.england.nhs.uk/wp-content/uploads/2015/10/ld-nat-imp-plan-oct15.pdf (Accessed 31 May 2020).

Landy, R. 1983. 'The use of distancing in drama therapy'. In: *The Arts in Psychotherapy*, 10(3) pp. 175–185. Science Direct Online: Elsevier.

Landy, R. 1985. 'The image of the mask: Implications for theatre and therapy'. In: *Journal of Mental Imagery*, 9(4) pp. 43–56. Publons Online.

McAlister, M. 2011. 'From transitional object to symbol: Spiderman in a dramatherapy group with mentally disordered offenders'. In Dokter, D., Holloway, P. & Seebohm, H. eds. *Dramatherapy and Destructiveness*, 145–156. East Sussex: Routledge.

Mental Health Act. 1983. (Amended 2007) Department of Health. Available at: www.legislation.gov.uk/ukpga/1983/20/contents (Accessed May 2020).

O'Connell, J. & Montague, T. 2016. 'The *'good enough'* couple. The containment of conflict and the roots of creativity in a music and art therapy group for forensic patients with intellectual disabilities and mental illness'. In: Rothwell, K. ed. *Forensic Arts Therapies Anthology and Practice and Research*. Great Britain: Free Publishing Limited.

Sajnani, N., Jewers-Dailley, K., Brillante, A., Puglisi, J. & Johnson, D.R. 2014. 'Animated learning by integrating and validating experience'. In: Sajnani, N. & Johnson, D.R. eds. *Drama Therapy Transforming Clinics, Classrooms and Communities*, 206–242. Springfield, IL: Charles C Thomas Publisher, Ltd.

Sinason, V. 1997. 'The learning disabled (mentally handicapped) offender'. In: Welldon, E. & Van Velsen, C. eds. *A Practical Guide to Forensic Psychotherapy*, 56–61. London: Jessica Kingsley Publishers.

Stokes, J. 1994. 'Problems in multidisciplinary teams: The unconscious at work'. In *Journal of Social Work Practice*, 8(2) pp. 161–167. London: Routledge.

Part 4

Coping with Change

Chapter 13

The Get Going Group

Dramatherapy Groups Supporting Adults with Learning Disabilities and Mental Ill Health after Discharge from Hospital

Jane Bourne and Simon Hackett

Introduction

Over one million adults in the UK are understood to have a learning disability, and just under half of these people experience mental illness. Over the years, this population has had long stays in hospital, been institutionalised with limited life choices and experienced restricted freedom and choice to develop skills (Delamothe 2013). NHS England (2017) set out to reform and transform the way health services are provided for people with a learning disability and mental illness by introducing the *Transforming Care* agenda. Its aim was to support people from hospitals into local communities and to avoid unnecessary hospital admissions. Unfortunately, despite policy changes, a report by MENCAP (2019) found both quality and access to community psychological provision were inadequate and people continued to be at risk of returning back to hospital.

This chapter details The Get Going Group: a dramatherapy group developed as a proactive approach to providing community support to people with a learning disability and mental ill health (Hackett & Bourne 2014) and a response to NHS England's *Transforming Care* (2015). The intervention was aimed at people who were at risk of being re-admitted to a specialist Treatment and Assessment Unit, which are specific hospitals with professionals who are trained to work with this population, and patients on a Treatment and Assessment Unit who were preparing for their discharge.

Initially, The Get Going Group was a pilot project, which has now been running for six years. A mixed-method approach was used to evaluate the intervention by gathering both quantitative and qualitative data in the form of pre- and post-outcome measures, a notes review and a focus group with support staff. Findings show that people who attend the group are less likely to be re-admitted to hospital and have improved quality of life through friendship building, increased communication skills and reduced anxiety. Further external benefits include reduced service use and monitoring a person's care and progress during the early stages of their discharge so that concerns can be highlighted with extra support being arranged.

DOI: 10.4324/9781003091783-18

This chapter details the work in three stages:

- The rationale and development of The Get Going Group.
- A case study.
- Data, findings and recommendations.

Rationale

The prevalence of mental health conditions in people with a learning disability is high, with estimates between 39% and 54% (Heslop et al. 2015). People with a learning disability and mental illness have a history of being institutionalised (Department of Health 2015, 2017) as well as being prescribed high amounts of psychotropic medications (Department of Health 2015). The Department of Health (2015) found 30,000 to 35,000 of adults with learning disabilities are taking psychotropic medicines for health conditions which here is no evidence that they have. In 2015 (Department of Health), *STOMP*, 'stopping over medication of people with a learning disability, autism or both', was introduced, which aimed to encourage therapeutic approaches rather than providing unnecessary medication for people with a learning disability. However, Mencap (2015) has found delays in developing community provision for people leaving hospital, particularly those which offer ongoing accessible therapeutic approaches.

Currently, there are limitations on what National Institute for Health and Care Excellence (NICE) (2016) recommends as interventions for this population. Three psychological options are documented to help support a person with a learning disability's mental health condition.

- Adapted Cognitive Behavioural Therapy (CBT) (1.9.5) to treat depression in people with mild learning disabilities.
- Relaxation Therapy to treat anxiety symptoms (1.9.6).
- Graded exposure for phobias (1.9.7).

Although these interventions can be beneficial, there is an expectation that a person has a certain level of cognitive ability, understanding and literacy level to access them. This means that for many people with a learning disability, these interventions, referred to as 'talking therapies', can be a challenge to engage with (Mencap 2019). The Arts Psychotherapies can offer creative mediums to explore challenges or distress when language and speech are limited. The British Psychological Society recognises dramatherapy as a psychosocial intervention which can benefit people when language acquisition and cognitions are impaired (Beail 2016). The Health and Care Professions Council (HCPC) *Standards of Proficiencies for Arts Therapists* describes dramatherapy as 'a unique form of psychotherapy in which creativity, play, movement, voice, storytelling, dramatisation, improvisation, art and the performance arts have a central relationship within the therapeutic relationship' (2018). NICE recommends dramatherapy to support a person's mental health

(CG178, recommendation 1.4.4.2, February 2014), yet this guidance does not specifically cover people with a learning disability.

As a response to the number of bed closures in recent years (Department of Health 2017) and the encouragement of accessible therapeutic interventions (NHS England 2015; Mencap 2019), Cumbria, Northumberland, Tyne and Wear NHS Foundation Trust set up two community dramatherapy groups, 'The Get Going Groups' (Hackett & Bourne 2014). These psychosocial interventions aimed to facilitate discharges, offer people at risk of returning to hospital a first point of contact as well as provide a facility where participants could share their difficulties with professionals.

The Participants

Referrals were adults aged 18 or over, who had a learning disability diagnosis and suffered with their mental health.

The Intervention

The Get Going Group uses a dramatherapy group model and is a manualised psychosocial intervention. The term 'psychosocial' is sometimes used to describe connections between the psychological aspects of experience and a wider social understanding (Bosgraaf et al 2020). Our intervention was devised using a treatment manual, so as to aid consistent delivery and help evaluate the groups. Manual-based psychological treatments have advantages for treatment fidelity, training and supervision in clinical strategies and techniques and are a defining feature of evidence-based treatments because they can be robustly evaluated (Wilson 1996).

The Get Going Groups are facilitated by a dramatherapist and a nurse and/or psychology assistant; delivered over 12 weekly sessions, each session lasting 90 minutes (Hackett & Bourne 2014). Referrals came from multidisciplinary teams in both community settings and those working on a Treatment and Assessment Unit. The dramatherapist and community nurses had previously worked with the patients who were referred, either on the Treatment and Assessment Unit or in the community, prior to the group starting. This was helpful as it offered people some continuity to their care.

Aims of The Get Going Group were:

- Support people leaving the hospital.
- Support people struggling with their mental health in the community.
- A space to support friendships with people who have similar lived experiences.
- Improve self-esteem, confidence and social learning.
- Explore roles people adopt within a group environment and the impact this has on themselves and others.
- Process experiences using expression and imagination through creative art forms.

The format and structure of the manualised intervention includes a welcome, a familiar warm-up or game at the beginning and ending of the session, a creative exercise addressing the main focus of the session and ending with reflections on a person's past week's events and plans for the future week ahead:

- Arrival – up to an hour before the start – to engage with other attendees, relax after journey to the group and contact with the space.
- Start of the group – sharing circle: sharing feelings. Recap from the last session and any connections made with personal circumstances after leaving the group.
- Warm-up games – designed to create a fun and relaxed atmosphere.
- Break – tea/coffee break to help people further relax and help with concentration.
- Main focus of the session – exploring and developing a person's individual six-part stories, using Lahad's (1999) six-part-story-making method and a variety of techniques/art forms as required. Prop building, story development, role-play, witnessing as well as a discussion involving a different story ending if deemed appropriate.
- Reflections – ending circle; a chance for clients to reflect on the activities and access their feelings about the session.

The game at the beginning of each session is usually the same each week, with the rationale that this structure would support familiarity, memory and reduce any anxieties around uncertainty and attendance. Games often included the use of a ball and checking people's names, again with the rationale to encourage familiarity, stimulate memory, urge turn-taking and help people with their coordination. An important part of the group was the inclusion of support staff and/or carers in the activities. Everyone, who attended the session, supporting a person with a learning disability, was seen as a group member, and this brought a new and helpful dynamic and understanding between participants and their care staff (Bourne et al 2020). Everyone at the sessions was encouraged to play the games and interact fully with all other members of the group, so as to promote equality within the environment. This support model is often termed 'mutual support' as it offers a space for positive relationships to be built, with the hope that this relationship development can then be extended further and repeated in any other community activities that a person might attend (Keyes 2012).

The main part of the sessions focused on generating individual stories. This story-development process used the 'the six-part story' method (Lahad 1999) with each person, including staff members, invited to develop stories through drawing six pictures: a character in a place or land, a goal, an obstacle, some help, what happens and an ending. The six-part story method is rooted in the practice of developing coping strategies and resilience for people experiencing ongoing stress (Lahad 1999). At The Get Going Group, each six-part story formed the basis for discussions, such as how characters experienced their task and what was the nature of the help to achieve an outcome (Hackett & Bourne 2014). Often, stories provided insight into a person's difficulties that they were experiencing or had previously experienced. This then provided opportunities for constructive dialogues to take place and appropriate help to be identified for the real world of a person's experiences and concerns. It was this form of support, within individuals' processes, which also enabled peer and mutual support to take place (Keyes 2012; Bourne et al 2020).

As the weeks progressed, the stories developed into small plays, with everyone contributing either playing specific roles or helping to build props. The use of these small plays and role-play was a way for people to share their challenges and experiences with others in the group. The process was both validating and liberating for the story maker, but there were also benefits for the people playing roles, and even for those watching the stories as an audience, through witnessing the enactment of a person's experience. After the plays had finished, both staff and group members were invited to consider how the characters dealt with their difficulties (Hackett & Bourne 2014). Reflections often gave insight into a person's inner thoughts and experiences.

If there was a negative outcome, or a difficult story ending, these were sensitively approached, with discussions about what could have been done differently and what further help could have been sought. Sometimes a play would be repeated with an adjustment to an ending, so as to give an alternative view point; this process was helpful for people to see possible changes rather than negative patterns repeating themselves. Having the whole group witness a person's experience and then support them was an empowering experience for the storyteller.

At the end of the 12 weekly sessions, the plan had been to *signpost* direct people to other community programs, interventions or activities. Unfortunately, there was limited choice or availability, which often meant people were referred back to The Get Going Group. The rationale for referrals returning to the group was not just cost-effective but actually linked with the group aims, in terms of a person's mental health being monitored and difficulties highlighted with reduced service use and unnecessary hospital admissions.

Case Study

'Sally' was one of the first people referred to The Get Going Group having recently left a Treatment and Assessment Unit, after a two-year stay. Sally was 34 years old and had a mild learning disability, re-occurring depression and anxiety, with episodes of self-harming and issues with food, such as restricting her intake. Over the years, she had received a number of periods of treatment in hospital, and she struggled to stay supported in the community for any length of time, due mainly to her self-harming behaviour. Sally had three children to whom she had visiting access. In the past, she had experienced domestic violence. After being discharged from the hospital to a new independent living environment in the community, Sally had received 24-hour support on a one-to-one basis.

Sally was initially quiet when attending the sessions. She would hide her arms from other group members because of the scars of a number of years of self-harming, often wearing her coat throughout the session. Although she was unable to start a dialogue with people and did not like speaking in front of anyone, she was willing to engage in most of the activities and particularly enjoyed art and story making.

One of the first six-part stories Sally shared with the group can be seen in Figure 13.1. The main character was Scratchy the cat who she told the group wanted to go fishing so that he could find some food. The 'help' *in the story* was finding somewhere that allowed him to catch fish, while the 'obstacle' was that the pond owner restricted fishing. The story evolved once Scratchy was able to get a fishing permit allowing him to fish there. This meant that Scratchy the cat was able to fish freely and eat again. Making the fishing permit prop seemed helpful to her and was used within the play.

Sally's Six-Part Story

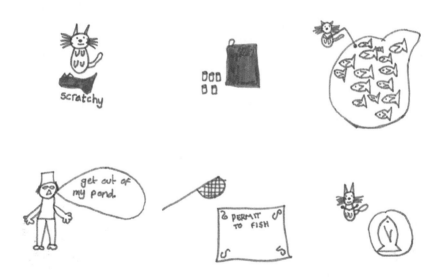

Figure 13.1 Sally's story.

Sally's story relates to her restricting her food intake when feeling anxious about something which she often couldn't identify. Most of the group's stories used fantasy characters as well as metaphors that related to a person's inner struggles. Sally never wished to role-play, or perform her story personally, and instead asked others to do this for her. She also never wanted to perform in other people's stories either, but was helpful in making props. The whole story-making process was helpful for Sally as it allowed her to be creative and to process what her story was communicating. Telling her story from a safe distance, using metaphorical characters and situations, allowed her the autonomy to share her feelings and struggles indirectly. Sharing her story with others in the group, who were helpful and supportive to her, allowed her to feel heard and accepted, begin to trust and validate her experiences.

Sally continued to come to the group for five years. She has not had another hospital admission in the time she has been attending. The group setting provided Sally with the opportunity to make friends whom she now meets outside the sessions and to maintain further regular activities, including visits with her children, Zumba classes and meals out with friends. Sally found The Get Going Group provided a place for her to share worries and concerns with the facilitators when in the group, with whom she had a positive relationship. At times, extra support was sourced for Sally, including regular phone calls or home visits from a psychologist. Without the intervention, and being able to regularly monitor Sally's mental health, a hospital admission might have been imminent. As Sally has continued to live in the community without disruptions to her care, with unnecessary hospital admissions, her confidence and self-esteem has improved. Over the years, Sally's confidence has grown so much that she now mentors new people attending the sessions, has a voluntary job one day a week, as a receptionist for an organisation that supplies support workers to people with learning disabilities, and has used her lived experience to help develop research projects.

Methods

A mixed-method approach was used to evaluate the intervention.

Quantitative data was collected in the form of self-reported questionnaires and administered to the participants at baseline and post-intervention. The purpose was to capture changes in self-esteem, anxiety and emotional well-being.

Outcome measures used included the following:

- The **Glasgow Anxiety Scale** *(GAS) and Glasgow Depression Scale (GDS)*, which are adapted self-rating scales looking at anxiety symptoms and depression symptoms, *respectively,* as used clinically and in research practice (Mindham & Espie 2003).
- The **Warwick-Edinburgh Emotional Well-Being Scale** (WEMWBS), used to measure mental well-being and responsiveness to changes occurring in a wide range of mental health interventions undertaken in different populations (Maheswaran et al 2012).
- The **CORE LD**, which is a simplified version from the CORE-OM, self-scoring with pictures to aid understanding (CORE IMS 2015).
- The **Rosenberg Self-Esteem Measure,** considered a reliable and valid quantitative tool for self-esteem assessment (Sinclair et al 2010).

Qualitative data was collected from a focus group using semi-structured interviews and a topic guide (Krueger 1994). The focus group included a sample of support staff and carers who had previously attended The Get Going Groups as support workers. Having insight from both group members and support staff was really helpful to further develop this intervention and devise the manual to advance practice. The focus group was audio recorded, transcribed and analysed by the drama-therapist delivering The Get Going Group. Ethical approval was granted by Leeds University. A 'Framework Analysis' approach was used to understand and interpret the themes (Braun & Clark 2006; Smith & Firth 2011), and these were then refined to eventually develop a conceptual framework to understand the findings.

Results

The outcome measures allowed us to see changes in a person's mental health and well-being over time pre- and post-intervention. The GDS showed a pre-treatment mean score below the clinical threshold for symptoms of depression, while measures post-treatment showed two group members had deteriorating symptoms, three had improved and for ten people there was 'no change'. This indicates no deterioration in symptoms over 24 sessions (refer to Figure 13.2). These outcomes were calculated using the 'Leeds reliable change indicator' (Morley & Dowzer 2014).

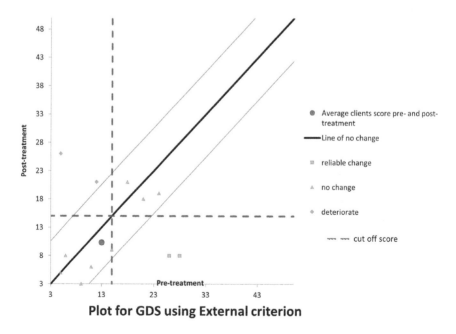

Plot for GDS using External criterion

Figure 13.2 Glasgow Depression Scale.

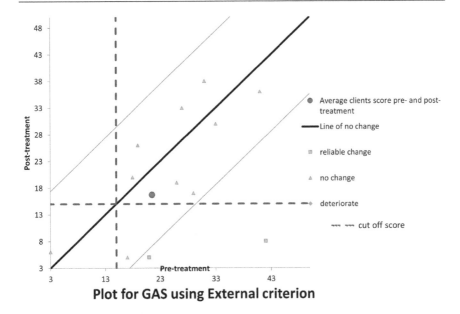

Plot for GAS using External criterion

Figure 13.3 Glasgow Anxiety Scale.

There was a mean decrease in people's scores on the GAS post-intervention from 21.6 to 19.5 post-group. A lowering of fear and anxiety, highlighted on the subsections of the tool, informs us that attending the intervention was beneficial overtime (refer to Figure 13.3) and reduced their anxiety.

The WEMWBS showed an overall group score increase of 7.1 post-group and indicates self-reporting improvements in a person's mental well-being. Findings using this tool suggest that people's well-being was maintained by attending the group and linked with the aims of the intervention.

Results from the self-reported Rosenberg Self-Esteem Measure, pre- and post-intervention were analysed with SPSS software (statistics version 27), using a paired T-test (Figure 13.4). This showed that a person's self-esteem significantly improved (mean = pre-intervention 21.35) following the intervention (mean = post-intervention 24.75). This was further confirmed with a P value of $P < 0.01$.

Importantly over a two-year period, there were only two people, out of 36 who attended The Get Going Group, who required a re-admission to hospital (Figure 13.5).

Results from the self-reported Rosenberg Self-Esteem Measure, pre- and post-intervention were analysed with SPSS software (statistics version 27), using a paired T-test (Figure 13.4). This showed that a person's self-esteem significantly improved (mean = pre-intervention 21.35) following the intervention (mean = post-intervention 24.75) (Figure 13.5): t (19) = −5.071, p < .001 (95% CI stands for Confidence Intervals. Upper = −1.997, Lower = −4.803).

Descriptives		Paired t-test				
Mean(SD)Pre	Mean(SD)Post	Mean(SD)	CI		T(df)	Sig(2-tld)
21.35(4.671)	24.75(3.432)	-3.40(2.998)	Lower	Upper	-5.071(19)	P<.001
			-4.803	-1.997		

Figure 13.4 T-Test.

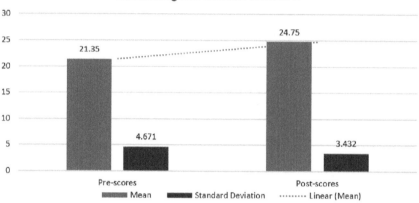

Figure 13.5 Mean and SD of RESM change pre and post intervention.

The qualitative results from the focus group have been published in an independent peer-reviewed journal (Bourne et al 2020). Themes include a 'hospital connection' and 'a new way of supporting'.

Support staff thought that there were clear benefits in having a connection with the hospital, as facilitators being familiar with participants helped reduce anxiety about attending The Get Going Group. This link with the hospital meant that professionals who also knew the participants could be reached by the facilitators, if extra support was thought to be useful. These included community nurses, psychologists or a person's psychiatrist. The dramatherapy groups were also seen as positive in that they offered a place to monitor transitions from hospital and also ongoing care in the community, as one support staff shared:

> She likes to have the connection with hospital still, because she is signed off from everybody. So, she hasn't got her psychiatrist, she hasn't got her social worker, she doesn't see anybody, so she comes and sees the facilitators here who still have a connection with the hospital.

> (Bourne et al 2019)

Through allowing participants an opportunity to attend further sessions after their first block of 12, the intervention can be seen to offer people both long- and short-term accessible support in the community and to overview a person's care.

> I think she's coming to a dip and I think coming to the Monday group when she's coming to a dip, I've got somebody to talk to too, so I will mention it to somebody.
>
> (Comment from support staff)

The environment of The Get Going Group offered a space for people to share stories, support one another, make connections through lived experiences and share their concerns and challenges with peers and professionals. It also offered added benefits to support staff too, as the setting and group structure meant staff were expected to join in the sessions as active group members rather than observers. This format seemed to reduce the division between staff and participants within a playful therapeutic structure. Feedback from support workers joining sessions was positive:

> I've worked for the Trust for thirty years now and its very different world to when I started, and you see groups like this getting together and people working together with clients and you don't have any us and them...... everybody is looking after each other. I think its brilliant – it's all coming together.
>
> (Bourne et al 2020)

Findings and Conclusion

There is a need for psychosocial community interventions that are accessible for people who have learning disabilities and mental ill health. Many hospitals have reduced inpatient beds (NHS England 2017), and medication has been re-evaluated (NHS England 2015), yet accessible supportive community interventions are still limited. The Get Going Group, as a psychosocial intervention, offers participants who attend, short or long term, in a supported and accessible environment, an opportunity to develop their skills, meet new people and a safe place to share their stories.

Having a relationship with the facilitators prior to attending a group can make attendance easier and less anxiety provoking for participants at the start of a new intervention. Having links with the hospital can offer a continuity of care, for a person with a learning disability moving back to communities and is important to reduce anxiety.

The Get Going Group supports staff, as it offers regular links with mental health professionals if any concerns about a person need highlighting. This process also helps reduce unnecessary service use, such as visits to the doctor or hospital admissions, as further care can be sought quickly and easily when concerns are highlighted.

The structure of The Get Going Group and support staff joining in activities rather than sitting on the outskirts observing sessions, allows staff to engage differently with the people they support and develop deeper relationships and engagements. It also gives support staff an opportunity to extend their own network through meeting other support staff who are attending.

Clinical benefits of attending The Get Going Group included reduced anxiety and depression, a person's quality of life being improved, significant improvements in their self-esteem and a low risk of 6% of being re-admitted to hospital.

Recommendations

Our findings have led us to make recommendations for future work in the community with people who have a learning disability and mental ill health:

Dramatherapy groups can offer ongoing support for people with a learning disability and mental illness after a hospital admission, as they are an accessible, cost-effective and psychosocial intervention able to monitor a person's ongoing care.

Including support staff in group sessions helps build in-depth relationships between staff and those they support.

Having a place where people with learning disabilities can meet weekly and link with professionals can reduce service use and unnecessary hospital admissions.

References

Beail, N. Ed. 2016. *Psychological therapies and people who have intellectual disabilities.* Retrieved from British Psychological Society website: /system/files/Public%20files/id_therapies.pdf

Bosgraaf, L., Spreen, M., Pattiselanno, K. & van Hooren, S. 2020. 'Art therapy for psychosocial problems in children and adolescents: a systematic narrative review on art therapeutic means and forms of expression, therapist behaviour, and supposed mechanisms of change'. In: *Frontiers in Psychology.* Sourced online: https://doi.org/10.3389/fpsyg.2020.584685

Bourne, J., Selman, M. & Hackett, S. 2020. 'Learning from support workers: Can a dramatherapy group offer a community provision to support changes in care for people with learning disabilities and mental health difficulties?' In: British Journal of Learning Disabi*li*ty. Volume 48, Issue 1, 59–68. Wiley Online Library.

Braun, B. & Clarke, V. 2006. 'Using thematic analysis in psychology'. In *Qualitative Research in Psychology.* Volume 3, Issue 2, 77–101. Taylor and Francis Online.

CORE IMS (Information Management System). 2015. https://www.coreims.co.uk [Accessed April 2021].

Delamothe, T. 2013. 'Learning from Winterbourne View'. In: *The British Medical Journal.* Volume 346, f433. London, UK: BMA.

Department of Health. 2015. *Transforming care for people with learning disabilities – next steps*. [online] Available at: https://www.england.nhs.uk/wp-content/uploads/2015/01/transform-care-nxt-stps.pdf [Accessed 22 August 2022].

Department of Health. 2017. *Allied health professions into action*. [online] Available at: https://www.england.nhs.uk/wp-content/uploads/2017/01/ahp-action-transform-hlth.pdf [Accessed 22 August 2022].

Hackett, S. & Bourne, J. 2014. 'The get going group: Dramatherapy with adults who have learning disabilities and mental health difficulties'. In *Dramatherapy*. Volume 36, Issue 1, 43–50. London: Routledge.

Health and Care Professions Council (HCPC) 2018. *Professions*. Retrieved from https://www.hcpc-uk.org/about-us/who-we-regulate/the-professions/ [Accessed 22 April 2018].

Heslop, P., Lauer, E. & Hoghton, M. 2015. 'Mortality in people with intellectual disabilities'. In: *The Journal for Applied Research in Intellectual Disability*. May Volume 28, Issue 5, 62–74. Wiley Online Library.

Keyes, C., Fredrickson, B. & Park, N. 2012. 'Positive psychology and the quality of life'. In: Land, K. (ed.) *Handbook of Social Indicators and Quality of Life Studies*. 99–112. New Yorker: Springer Editors.

Krueger, R.A. 1994. *Focus groups: A practical guide for applied research* (2nd ed.). Thousand Oaks, CA: Sage Publications.

Lahad, M. 1999. 'The use of dramatherapy with crisis intervention groups, following mass evacuation'. In: *The Arts in Psychotherapy*. Volume 26, Issue 1, 27–33. Science Direct Online.

Maheswaran, H., Weich, S. & Powell, J. 2012. 'Evaluating the responsiveness of the Warwick Edinburgh Mental Well-Being Scale (WEMWBS): Group and individual level analysis'. In: *Health Quality Life Outcomes*. Volume 10, 156. London: BioMed Central.

Mencap. 2015. *Changing attitudes to learning disability: A review of the evidence*. https://www.mencap.org.uk/sites/default/files/2016-08/Attitudes_Changing_Report.pdf

Mencap 2019. *What is a learning disability?* [online] Available at: https://www.mencap.org.uk/learning-disability-explained/what-learning-disability [Accessed April 2019].

Mindham, J. & Espie, C.A. 2003. 'Glasgow anxiety scale for people with an Intellectual Disability (GAS-ID): Development and psychometric properties of a new measure for use with people with mild intellectual disability'. In: *The Journal of Intellectual Disability Research*. Volume 47, Issue 1, 22–30. Wiley Online Library.

Morley, S. & Dowzer, C.N. 2014. *Manual for the Leeds reliable change indicator: Simple Excel(tm) applications for the analysis of individual patient and group data*. Leeds: University of Leeds.

National Institute for Health and Care Excellence – NICE (2016). *Mental health problems in people with learning disabilities: prevention, assessment and management | Guidance and guidelines* Retrieved from https://www.nice.org.uk/guidance/ng54 [Accessed 22 April 2018].

NHS England. 2015. *Stopping over medication of people with a learning disability, autism or both (STOMP)* https://www.england.nhs.uk/learning-disabilities/improving-health/stomp/ [Accessed 22 April 2022].

NHS England. 2017. *Transforming Care Agenda*. Retrieved 7 April 2019 from https://www.england.nhs.uk/wp-content/uploads/2017/02/model-service-spec-2017.pdf

Sinclair, S.J., Blais, M.A., Gansler, D.A., Sandberg, E., Bistis, K. & LoCicero, A. 2010. 'Psychometric properties of the Rosenberg Self-Esteem Scale: overall and across demographic groups living within the United States'. In: *Evaluation & the Health Professions*. Volume 33, Issue 1, 56–80. New York: Sage.

Smith, J. & Firth, J. 2011. 'Qualitative data analysis: Application of the framework approach'. In: *Nurse Researcher*. Volume 18, Issue 2, 52–62. RCNi Plus Online.

Wilson, G.T. 1996. 'Manual-based treatments: the clinical application of research findings'. In: *Behaviour Research and Therapy*. Volume 34, Issue 4, 295–314. Science Direct Online.

Chapter 14

Making Connections through Life and Death

Jessie Ellinor and Amy Keenan

Introduction

This chapter offers perspectives from two different organisations: a special needs primary school and Noah's Ark Children's Hospice (https://www.noahsarkhospice. org.uk). It demonstrates how dramatherapy can provide opportunities for children with special educational needs and disabilities (SEND) to feel supported to understand and express feelings connected with loss and bereavement. It 'signposts' resources and outlines practical examples of stories and interventions used to support children and their families with their grief. This chapter integrates grief theories including the '5 Stage Model of Grief' (Kubler-Ross 1969), the 'Four Tasks of Mourning' (Worden 1991), 'continuing bonds' (Klass et al 1996), the Dual Process Model (Stroebe & Schut 1999) and techniques in grief therapy (Neimeyer & Cacciatore 2016).

This chapter highlights how the ethos of organisations, where the emphasis 'to put the child at the centre' of all they do, use dramatherapists as valuable resources. This includes working together to create guidelines and policies, which support their staff and families to feel equipped to be part of the grieving process alongside the child. Throughout this chapter, challenges related to developmental understanding, communication difficulties and emotional barriers are explored to ensure bereavements are appropriately communicated.

Into the Unknown – Enabling Grief through Creativity

As creative arts therapists, we are skilled in using the art form to help encourage individuals explore the unknown. We 'pack' an imaginary, sometimes literal bag, full of things we think might be useful for the therapeutic 'journey'. However, the emphasis is on the companionship to embark on the quest, often heading into shadows with the client. This is even more important when working with grief and people with learning disabilities, 'Death and disability is the double taboo...' (Winston's Wish – New SEND specialist bereavement book launched nationwide 2019a). Often from birth, stages of development, including the forming of attachment patterns, are more complex. Therefore, the permanent loss of a loved one is

DOI: 10.4324/9781003091783-19

challenging on multiple levels. Therapy may not yield answers to confusing questions, and comprehension may feel intangible, but awareness must be demonstrated that '[all] children, regardless of their cognitive skills, are affected by the death of someone they were close to' (Helton 2017, 26). Thus, it is important to ensure information is appropriately accessible, attuning to the feelings and responses that emerge.

As dramatherapists, this journey is often navigated through image, stories, metaphor, movement and enactments. When coming to grief work, the use of common euphemisms, such as 'they've passed away and gone to a better place', can be misleading. In her own experience of bereavement, Lipsky (2013) notes that, for a person with autism, the greatest impact of a death often comes through changes in routine and structure. She recommends 'be blunt even if that seems cold and insensitive [...] Present the facts as you have them' (85). This is echoed by Blackman (2003) who states:

> Abstract images and concepts are often used in therapy, but this may be very confusing for a client with a learning disability. The therapist may need to begin by communicating using very concrete language [...] Puppets or dolls can be used to help the client tell a story or to express something difficult.
>
> (94–95)

In 'We All Grieve', Winston's Wish (2019b) authors identify interventions suited to differing 'functioning' ages of cognitive development for people with special needs. Emphasis at each stage is focused on keeping communication accessible and open. The Child Bereavement UK website states, 'those with autistic spectrum difficulties (ASD)…may not respond to the death of someone close to them in the same way as other children but this does not mean they are not grieving' (Child Bereavement UK 2018a). This highlights the importance of attunement, and the need to intuitively notice responses from individuals, following how these interactions may differ in emotion, energy and communication.

Use of the Art Forms

The ritualised structure often used in dramatherapy sessions can enable people with learning disabilities to feel safe and focused, supportively guiding and aiding individuals through the process of grief. 'Your knowledge of each individual child will be invaluable in finding creative ways to help them understand, communicate and express their feelings' (Seesaw Schools Pack – A guide to supporting pupils through bereavement 2018).

Dramatherapists are equipped practitioners using psychodynamic and analytical theories alongside intuitive and feeling functions, to ground unconscious communications. Interventions such as 'Intensive Interaction', founded by Hewett (2011) encourage attunement and connection. 'Following a bereavement the child may make some different sounds, …releasing their emotions. When the adult copies…

the child sees they have been listened to and that they are not the only person feeling the way they do' (Winston's Wish, *We All Grieve* 2019b, 27). Dooman (2012) and Cattanach (1997) note that witnessing and taking part in clients' play and stories creatively enables exploration of memories, encouraging individuals to consider the meaning of their lived experiences. This links to Kessler's (2019) sixth stage of grieving, which he added to the five stages initiated by Kubler-Ross (1969). This stage encourages meaning-making after a death, to support transformation and hope from grief.

Containment through Policies and Procedures

When any death occurs, thinking can become impaired. 'Stuckness' and uncertainty of what to do 'for the best' can 'disable' the sense of where to begin. Policies and procedures can often be helpful, providing transparency, clarity and structure. Both the school and the children's hospice have developed policies which hold this in mind, to ensure individuals with learning disabilities do not find themselves a 'forgotten mourner' (Winston's Wish 2019). They provide clear diagrams and steps guiding the professional who has been alerted of the death, what to 'do' next. A SEND headteacher commented:

> There is nothing more daunting than receiving the news that a child or member of school staff has died. One thing that helps me to think straight is our Bereavement Policy. It tells me very clearly what to do and who to contact. It is a huge comfort at a very distressing time.

Bereavement policies within our organisations are a working document that continue to evolve, as different ideas and difficulties emerge. Tiered systems of who to contact and guidance of what support systems and interventions are available enables consistent containment for challenging and emotive situations, supporting staff, families and pupils, making the 'unmentionable manageable'.

Therapeutic Interventions

Class sessions following the Death of a Child

In the special needs school, a set of sessions were developed, to support classes after the death of a child or member of staff. Following a letter sent home informing parents, three sessions are available, using ritual dramatherapy structures, stories, music and play. All resources are accessible for staff and families to utilise, stored in a 'Bereavement Box', which is kept alongside other 'life changes' resource boxes: puberty, new baby and divorce. A co-facilitating structure supports shared planning and organisation. Sessions were designed to be held by the dramatherapist and/or teacher (leading any storytelling and narrative elements) and/or a music therapist or musician (leading the songs and music). Responses from the children and staff become intuitively embedded throughout the sessions. The focus, warm up and grounding are repeated each week, using songs written by music therapists to provide familiar bookends to the sessions. A 'social story' (Gray & Garand 1993) with objects is used to explain the death, while photos and activities are shared to help remember the person who has died. Stories such as *The Day the Sea Went Out and Didn't Come Back* (Sunderland 2003), *Rabbityness* (Empson 2012) or *Gentle Willow* (Mills 2003) are explored using puppets, toys, art and sensory objects. At the end of each session, the group takes part in an activity the person enjoyed: making music, blowing bubbles, dancing to a particular song.

After co-facilitating sessions in class, a profound and multiple learning disabilities (PMLD) class teacher (2020) reflected:

> The atmosphere created was calm and inclusive, with children becoming more involved as the weeks progressed. The sessions were especially helpful for staff, giving them space to share important feelings, helping to remember the child, validating the emotional nature of the work we do.

Following initial experiences, it became apparent how challenging the sessions were to contain, and so a co-working format was utilised. Sessions understandably were often met with unconscious resistance: difficulty in timetabling, frenetic concentration from staff and a sense of people suddenly feeling deskilled in their ability to 'be' (with the children or material). It became evident that running sessions too soon felt disruptive, with staff still in shock. A pre-session meeting helped empower staff to voice any concerns, reminding them they can 'shed tears […] use symbols to communicate how [they] are feeling, but also to reassure the child that [they] are OK and [their] response is natural' (Child Bereavement UK 2018b). Additionally, therapeutic sessions for staff at the end of the day became optional but highly valued by members who attended. A SEND teacher said this:

> The death of a child in my class was absolutely heart-breaking. In the class team sessions after school, I was able to open up with my team, express feelings and share stories about the little girl who had sadly died. These sessions also helped me to stay connected to and support the family.

Memory Boxes

Staff within the school and hospice benefit from a space to share memories together, creating 'continuing bonds' for themselves and the family. Memory boxes (Macmillan Cancer Support 2020), filled with sensory objects, photos and personalised messages, allow a creative, literal and symbolic container to share memories of time with the child. This activity can be beneficial and comforting for both the family and the staff in their processing and bereavement experience.

When working with a child with PMLD, pre- and post- bereavement of her brother, sensory items in her memory box, relating to physical interaction between the siblings, were utilised every week in dramatherapy. These became physical and symbolic 'parting gifts' from her brother after his death. A parent commented on their child's grief:

> Her grief was so very deep. Normally a child without speech or any verbal communication, she wailed for weeks. I think the items in the box chose us. It was important the box contained things to; see, touch, hear, smell and sometimes even taste. After her brother's death, the house was so silent, we didn't realise just how much noise his different breathing machines made. She used to go to his room to find him and stand in the space where the oxygen concentrator used to be. We made recordings for her memory box, so she could press to hear the sounds, along with a piece of sheepskin she loved feeling when she was close to him, specific hair lotion, which kept his curls gorgeous and fairy lights, because he responded best to light and reflection, so was never far from twinkles and sparkles. I think they were comforting for her.

Family work following the death of a child

> Siobhan was four years old when she died of Neuroblastoma. Using the residential, community based, and end of life care provided by Noah's Ark Hospice, her family was supported to transfer her from hospital to her family home. The hospice provided a cold blanket (a lightweight, cooling blanket with a portable machine to delay deterioration of the body after death). This enabled precious time for her immediate and extended family, to spend a number of nights with her. During this period, dramatherapy work entailed creating a 'family tree', using Siobhan's handprint along with prints from family members. The symbol of the tree, with its connecting branches, highlighted the strong family bond of love, with their child forever part of this connection. Each individual's palms represented the leaves and colours were chosen to personalise each section. This activity allowed children and parents, with different levels of understanding of death and dying, to process and begin a continuing bond (Klass et al 1996), with the tree now a key part of their family home. Continuing bonds encourage, instead of severing bonds, with the deceased; attachments are relocated in 'objects' (including memories and story sharing) to help find resolution in grief. This was demonstrated further in fingerprints taken from Siobhan to create memorial jewellery for the family.

Continuing and externalising attachments through creative methods forms part of an epigenetic framework, developed more recently by Neimeyer and Cacciatore (2016). This developmental model of grief discusses the incorporation of both internal experience and external behaviours, shaped by biogenetic, personal-agentic, dyadic-relational and cultural-linguistic factors. Many of these factors are intertwined with a person or child's disability in terms of genetic and environmental factors. This theory encompasses three stages of grief: reacting, reconstructing and reorienting. They note that those with disabilities may find themselves stuck for a longer time period, or more intensely, in the process of grief, similar to Erikson's (1958) conception of 'crises', where there are tensions between two opposing factors. This could be due to a lack of emotional and social awareness, low cognitive abilities and inability to communicate. It may also be hindered by professionals' lack of awareness that those with disabilities may be undergoing the same stages of grief as anyone.

Parents' protective concerns for children surrounding death can reflect their own fears and denial. When considering those with disabilities therefore, dramatherapy can be a useful intervention to help parents support themselves and to support their child. Dramatherapy, unlike life, enables an open platform to explore many different scenarios, with techniques such as character work and improvisation. It creates an opportunity to 'rehearse' experiences without lifelong consequences. Coleman and Kelly (2012) state 'Dramatherapy sessions can provide an opportunity to explore the theme of maximising life in the face of death' (121).

Alongside the distancing and creative techniques, strong and sensitive direct communications with the family are also essential. For example, when creating a bespoke social story for the child, using family photos and wording to explain that someone they are close to is becoming increasingly unwell or has died. Additional copies can be made for the child to have in class and at home. Close communication with the family keeps information as accurate and as current as possible for the child, adding and amending pages to help aid understanding. Feedback from parents were:

> The book was a very useful tool to explain what had happened, allowing consistency and avoiding possible confusion. There were times she didn't want to look at the book and times when she'd snuggle in closely to have the story read to her…I loved that she had different reactions at different times. I hoped it was an indication of awareness and choice. The book was greatly useful for other family members. I didn't want them to think they'd upset me by talking about what had happened; the book was always accessible and as time went on we chose a place on the shelf so we always know it is OK to talk about it all.

By incorporating a mixture of factual information and spontaneous dramatherapy interventions, the therapist can attune and follow the client's lead. Books such as *A Jumble of Knotted Thoughts* (Back Pocket Teacher 2018) have been designed to share developmentally appropriate bereavement information, with the sensory needs of children with learning disabilities in mind. Should the sessions be pre-bereavement work, stories such as *The Gentle Willow* (Mills 2003), which uses themes in connection with illness, a degenerative condition and death, can be gradually explored over weeks, utilising puppets and sensory objects, alongside the client's individual book. Gersie (1991) and Blackman (2003) advocate personal stories being explored through the ritual, myth and language of traditional stories. This provides distancing and involvement, encouraging subjective feelings and themes of death and dying to be relocated through projection. 'Storytellers create a semblance of a stable and secure environment into which they will later introduce the foreboding elements that carry the message or the bit of unbearable knowledge that has to be imparted to the audience' (Gersie 1991, 16). Narratives can then offer new perspectives 'the time will come when we will recognise her in another way. Maybe it will be in a song from the wind. Maybe it will be in the dance of the butterflies' (Mills 2003, 21).

Often emotional responses may not seem present for a long time, if at all. 'For a person with autism it may well be after the six month or year mark that they are hit with profound sadness and actually begin grieving the loss on an emotional level' (Lipsky 2013, 51). As therapists, we must work hard to understand the direct attachment experiences the child had with the person who has died (Bowlby 1970). We must be vigilant to notice when 'stuckness' (Kubler-Ross 1969) may be present and strive where appropriate, to establish that the child understands that continuing bonds remain, connecting them to their loved one (Klass et al 1996).

Sustained time and space are required for a trusting relationship to develop between the client and therapist. This aids intuitive responses and attunement to small changes within the client's emotional world.

Addy, a 10-year-old girl, with complex needs, including attention-deficit hyperactivity disorder (ADHD) and cerebral palsy, attended weekly dramatherapy sessions through the hospice. During these sessions, her grandfather died following a brief illness. Connecting this experience with Worden's (1991) Task 1 – 'to accept the reality of the loss', at first Addy appeared fine and used concrete thinking to understand that 'grandad was here and now, not here'. This was closely followed by Neimeyer and Cacciatore's (2016) first stage 'reacting', involving a 'crisis' of 'connection vs isolation' and Worden's Task 2 – 'to experience the pain of grief'. Although Addy was able to name that grandad was no longer here, she often found it hard to fully understand what had happened. She struggled to regulate her emotional responses, accompanied with high levels of anxiety. These needed some gentle, sustained attention. Due to her complex needs, Addy often used 'adult based responses', which masked her own grief. This lack of connection and indeed isolation, compounded by her disabilities, made this stage in her grief a 'crisis'. Therefore, her dramatherapy sessions (which had primarily focused on hospital projected play with dolls) became more intense, with explorations of illness and death. This distancing technique of projected play gave Addy an outlet and a way to communicate the difficult feelings and grief surrounding her grandad. To help integrate these thoughts, a worry doll was used at the end of each session. This enabled playful, yet direct methods to explore emotions visually and verbally, through writing and speaking. Using baby dolls, Addy was able to reflect on feelings of sadness, anger and shock about her grandad dying; key emotions which were able to be expressed in this way to support her cognitive developmental stage of understanding, enabling her to process what had happened.

Giving Addy time and a creative therapeutic space for her to emerge from this crisis was key. Being aware of her disabilities and what tools she used most effectively to express herself enabled opportunities to transition from 'reacting' to the stages of 'reconstructing and reorienting' (Neimeyer & Cacciatore 2016). Using

Stroebe and Schut's (1999) 'Dual Process Model', Addy explored loss-orientated and restoration-orientated stressors, similar to a butterfly relying on both its wings to fly and progress. Zech (2016) discusses how the attachment behavioural system is activated in bereavement, due to the death signalling the loss of an attachment figure. With Addy's complex needs, she often presented with insecure attachment patterns, due to the higher levels of dependency required on others (Clegg & Lansdall-Welfare 1995). With this in mind, areas where she focused more on loss-orientated strategies, benefitted from encouragement and support for more restorative approaches, such as through her play.

The sessions discussed in this chapter sensitively follow the 'progress' of the clients, involving clear communication with family and staff, who are also acutely aware of the child's emotional behaviours. Endings are carefully planned, with an understanding that underpinning therapeutic sessions, there is an aim 'to integrate all aspects of life and death in one human cycle, which has a beginning, middle and an end' (Coleman & Kelly 2012, 124). With this in mind, at the hospice and school, sessions are also made available for children with life-limiting conditions.

Life-Limiting Care

It has been found that the levels of anxiety are higher in those children with life-limiting conditions in comparison to those chronically ill, even when undergoing the same amount of hospital treatments. In her research, Spinetta and Maloney (1975) found anxiety and isolation also extended to when the child was no longer in hospital, and even during remission, for leukaemia children. Due to lack of resources elsewhere, the therapists at the hospice are often needed to support cancer patients. It has been highlighted that cancer and anxiety are common health problems of people with learning disabilities (Blair 2009). This may explain the above average prevalence of these comorbidities in the palliative and therapeutic sectors. In their ethnographic study, Tuffrey-Wijne et al (2009) concluded that high levels of anxiety are found in this population who had cancer, arguing the vital need for increased support and clearer communication. While this is important for professionals involved in their care, it is also key for parents and other family members.

Importance of Remembering – Continuing Bonds

A prominent theme with death and grief work is that it can at times feel invisible, often being managed in confidential sessions, behind closed doors. Schools and communities may need encouragement to ensure they are aware of support available and are able to share news appropriately, through a mixture of words, images and sign language/makaton. Using inspiration from other cultures, such as the colourful and celebratory Mexican tradition of 'Día de Muertos' (Day of the Dead), can encourage an impetus for a community to come together to remember and celebrate those whose lives we all miss. A former SEND headteacher told us:

Introducing Celebration of Life Days was such an important part of our community calendar. These days gave us an interval from the rawness of bereavement to celebrate the wonderful lives the children had lived.

As with the class sessions, events must be carefully planned, to accommodate the needs of the participants; sensory activities, stories and music sessions. Photos and brief words can be used to explain and help connect each activity to memories of the individuals. Ensuring staff know they have permission to authentically communicate feelings validates 'children need to understand that giving expression is both normal and healthy' (Chadwick 2012, 11). In both institutions, families of those who have died can be invited to attend a 'Remembering Assembly' or annual 'Memory Day'. Adding an engraved symbol to a memorial monument, such as a tree with engraved leaves (Figure 14.1.), or a ceramic butterfly memory trail (Figure 14.2), can encourage further memory making and continuing bonds for the family. Families may take comfort from revisiting these places of remembrance.

I'll always love that tree. A physical thing where families can place their little ones name or date or image in a supportive and tender environment.

(Parent Carer 2020)

Figure 14.1 Memory tree.

Figure 14.2 Ceramic butterflies.

Ongoing support may be offered following the death of a child using memory making and bereavement-based tools including quilted memory books and support groups.

Obstacles, Challenges and Support

Supporting clients with learning disabilities with themes of death and dying encompasses many obstacles. Culture and gender are further interlinking factors which need to be considered alongside a learning disability, demonstrating there is no one 'right' way to grieve, and that everyone and every loss is different. At times, our aim to work with transparency can be challenged by different cultural and religious beliefs. This may occur where it is not permitted to speak of death, before the death has occurred. Creative techniques can be useful to support individuals in this journey towards death, while respecting the family's faith. Furthermore, translators may be useful to overcome language barriers, to ensure clear communication at this difficult time.

When supporting clients with learning disabilities and organisations with bereavement needs, it is important to acknowledge the difficulties encountered when nothing feels 'good enough', especially when met with resistance and adversity. Other professionals may feel uncomfortable and deskilled, reluctant to engage and support discussions around death and dying, especially surrounding the death of a child. This is common, therefore training for staff is essential to enable them to feel confident in their own abilities and knowledge. Additionally, ensuring clear communications are in place helps to contain misunderstandings or expectations.

While being mindful of staff's emotional availability to participate in bereavement-related activities, the therapy team also have to take heed, ensuring their own psychological capacity to therapeutically contain themes of death and dying is robust. There are times when this will not be the case. Supporting and facing death can naturally affect therapists working in this area. It is therefore vital to use resources to help to separate oneself from work, otherwise this area can imperil our own mental well-being. Please find an example below, which demonstrates how we employ processing techniques to regulate our own connections.

Amy's Poem: 'Little Bird'

First there was pain with little or no gain,
Second there was fire, bursting and ravenous,
free and flexible,
Third there was beauty, strength and drive,
This princess needs no saviour of any kind,
Fourth there was mischief, cheek and glee,
Light that overcame the shadow,
When it took flight.
But those wings, they broke and crumpled,
and yet she flew and flew,
and flew and flew,
until there was no flight in sight,
And the shadows returned,
But this time as an old friend,
an acquaintance, an acceptance,
And our little bird it flew once more,
Softly and higher, higher and higher,
and settled in the sky,
Shining, and reminding us,
of our drive of flight,
Even in the darkest of times.
Little bird, little star, forever in my heart.

Promoting self-awareness and reflection is key to enable a healthy working mind, individually and collectively for those involved.

Conclusion

'Usually hopelessness in the face of impending death is interspersed with hopefulness' (Judd 1993, 196).

This chapter has highlighted why clients with learning disabilities need developmentally appropriate information to support their processing, in the pre- and post-bereavement stages. Dramatherapy, with its adaptive and flexible approach, is an effective intervention during various stages of grief. In addition, collaborative work with therapists, staff and families can enable aspects surrounding grief to be seen, heard, felt, held and connected.

As reflected in our use of the sensory objects, memory boxes and social stories, we have found symbols, visual aids, play and story to be particularly effective in our professional practice, when working with clients with learning disabilities. It is important to be culturally informed and aware of different religious beliefs and practices regarding death, alongside using clear and understandable forms of communication for those with additional needs. Concrete words such as dead, death and dying can diminish a lot of confusion, especially for those with early cognitive functioning disabilities. This chapter has demonstrated how dramatherapists are a useful resource within organisations, enabling and supporting the practicalities needed to educate children with learning disabilities around all aspects of bereavement.

A death or loss can have a ripple effect, often touching the lives of many; therefore, working with death requires a holistic approach. Everyone is different in their grief, and every loss is different; dramatherapy offers a bespoke therapeutic intervention 'when words are not enough', to support clients to process their loss and grieve in their own way and time. Dramatherapy continuously evolves and adapts, to creatively walk alongside clients, as well as others affected systemically during stages of grief.

This chapter is dedicated to the children and families we meet during our dramatherapy bereavement work, as well as our own personal continuing bonds.

References

Back Pocket Teacher. 2018. https://backpocketteacher.co.uk (Accessed 16 September 2020).

Blackman, N. 2003. *Loss and Learning Disability.* London: Worth Publishing Ltd.

Blair, J. 2009. 'Common health problems of people with learning disabilities'. In: *British Journal of Family Medicine.* https://www.bjfm.co.uk/blog/common-health-problems-of-people-with-learning-disabilities-blog (Accessed 24 April 2020).

Bowlby, J. and Parkes, C.M. 1970. 'Separation and loss within the family'. In: Anthony, E.J. & Koupernick, C. Eds. *The Child in His Family.* International Yearbook of Child Psychiatry and Allied Professions. 197–216. New York: Wiley.

Cattanach, A. 1997. *Children's Stories in Play Therapy.* London: Jessica Kingsley Publishers.

Chadwick, A. 2012. *Talking about Death and Bereavement in School.* London and Philadelphia, PA: Jessica Kingsley Publishers.

Child Bereavement UK. 2018a. *Supporting bereaved children and young people with Autism Spectrum Disorders (ASD).* https://www.childbereavementuk.org/Handlers/Download.ashx?IDMF=e99e1f53-01c0-4112-bfa4-e2a58dfb4e24 (Accessed 18 April 2020).

Child Bereavement UK. 2018b. *Supporting bereaved children and young people with special educational needs.* https://www.childbereavementuk.org/information-bereaved-children-with-special-needs (Accessed 25 June 2020).

Clegg, J.A. & Lansdall-Welfare, R. 1995. 'Attachment and learning disability: a theoretical review informing three clinical interventions'. In: *Journal of Intellectual Disability Research.* Volume 39, 295–305. Wiley Online Library.

Coleman, A. & Kelly, A. 2012. 'Beginning, middle, end, beginning: dramatherapy with children who have life-limiting conditions and with their siblings.' In: Leigh, L., Giersch, I., Dix, A. & Haythorne, D. eds. *Dramatherapy with Children, Young People and Schools: Enabling Creativity, Sociability, Communication and Learning.* 117–125. London: Routledge.

Dooman, R. 2012. 'Looking for meaning with bereaved families: 'Bring back my Daddy' and other stories.' In: Leigh, L., Giersch, I., Dix, A. & Haythorne, D. eds. *Dramatherapy with Children, Young People and Schools: Enabling Creativity, Sociability, Communication and Learning.* 98–105. London: Routledge.

Empson, J. 2012. *Rabbityness.* Swindon: Child's Play International Ltd.

Erikson, E.H. 1958. *Young Man Luther: A Study in Psychoanalysis and History.* New York: Norton.

Gersie, A. 1991. *Storytelling in Bereavement – Dragons Fight in the Meadow.* London and Philadelphia: Jessica Kingsley Publishers.

Gray, C. & Garand, J. 1993. 'Social stories: Improving responses of individuals with autism with accurate social information'. In *Focus on Autistic Behavior.* Volume 8, Issue 1, 1–10. https://carolgraysocialstories.com/wp-content/uploads/2015/10/Social-Stories-Improving-Responses-of-Students-with-Autism-with-Accurate-Social-Information.pdf

Helton, S. 2017. *Remembering Lucy.* London and Philadelphia, PA: Jessica Kingsley Publishers.

Hewett, D., Firth, G., Barber, M. & Harrison, T. 2011. *The Intensive Interaction Handbook.* London: Sage.

Judd, D. 1993. 'Communicating with dying children'. In Dickenson, D. & Johnson, M. eds. *Death, Dying and Bereavement.* 192–198. London: Sage Publications.

Kessler, D. 2019. *Finding Meaning: The Sixth Stage of Grief.* New York: Ebury Publishing.

Klass, D., Silverman, P.R. & Nickman, S.L. 1996. *Continuing Bonds – New Understandings of Grief.* Philadelphia, PA, Levittown and London: Taylor and Francis.

Kubler Ross, E. 1969. *On Death and Dying.* New York: The Macmillan Company.

Lipsky, D. 2013. *How People with Autism Grieve, and How to Help – An Insider Handbook.* London and Philadelphia, PA: Jessica Kingsley Publishers.

Macmillan Cancer Support. https://www.macmillan.org.uk/cancer-information-and-support (Accessed 03 June 2020).

Mills, J.C. 2003. *Gentle Willow – A Story for Children about Dying.* Washington, DC: Magination Press.

Neimeyer, R.A. & Cacciatore, J. eds. 2016. *Techniques of Grief Therapy, Assessment and Intervention.* New York: Routledge.

Noah's Ark Children's Hospice. https://www.noahsarkhospice.org.uk (Accessed 02 June 2020).

Seesaw Schools Pack. 2018. *A guide to supporting pupils through bereavement.* https://www.seesaw.org.uk/wp-content/uploads/2020/04/SCHOOLS-PACK-PDF-1.pdf (Accessed 20 April 2020).

Spinetta, J. & Maloney, J. 1975. 'Death anxiety in the outpatient leukemic child'. In: *Pediatrics.* Volume 56, Issue 6, 1035–1037. Itasca, IL: American Academy of Pediatrics.

Stroebe, M. & Schut, H. 1999. 'The dual process model of coping with bereavement: rationale and description.' In: *Death Studies.* Volume 23, Issue 3, 197–224. Doi:10.1080/074811899201046. Taylor and Francis Online.

Sunderland, M. 2003. *The Day the Sea Went out and Didn't Come Back.* London: Taylor and Francis.

Tuffrey-Wijne, I., Bernal, J., Hubert, J., Butler, G. & Hollins, S. 2009. 'People with learning disabilities who have cancer: an ethnographic study'. In: *The British Journal of General Practice: The Journal of the Royal College of General Practitioners.* Volume 59, Issue 564, 503–509. London: The Royal College of General Practitioners.

Winston's Wish. 2019a. *New SEND specialist bereavement book.* https://www.winston-swish.org/send-specialist-bereavement-book/ (Accessed 04 June 2020).

Winston's Wish. 2019b. *We All Grieve: Supporting Bereaved Children Who Have Special Educational Needs/Disabilities.* Gloucester: Winston's Wish.

Worden, J.W. 1991. *Grief Counselling and Grief Therapy.* London: Routledge.

Zech, E. 2016. 'The dual process model in grief therapy.' In: Neimeyer, R.A. ed. *Techniques of Grief Therapy, Assessment and Intervention.* 19–24. New York: Routledge.

Chapter 15

Emerging from That Storm

Reflections on a School-Based Arts Therapy Team's Response to the Covid-19 Pandemic

Rebecca Blake and Georgina Harris

I heard that we are in the same boat.
   But it's not that.
   We are in the same storm, but not in the same boat.
   Your ship can be shipwrecked and mine might not be.
   Or vice versa.
   For some, quarantine is optimal: a moment of reflection, of reconnection…
   Some were in their 'home office'. Others looking through trash to survive…
   So, friends, we are not in the same boat.
   We are going through a time when our perceptions and needs are completely different. And each one will emerge, in his own way, from that storm.
   It is very important to see beyond what is seen at first glance. Not just looking, more than looking, seeing.
   See beyond the political party, beyond biases, beyond the nose on your face. Do not judge the good life of the other, do not condemn the bad life of the other.
   Don't be a judge.
   Let us not judge the one who lacks, as well as the one who exceeds him. We are on different ships looking to survive. Let everyone navigate their route with respect, empathy and responsibility.

This is an extract from a version of a poem written by an anonymous author, inspired by a tweet from columnist and author Damian Barr (Barr 2020), during the height of the Covid-19 pandemic. Subsequently shared on Barr's Twitter feed, it has been used worldwide to highlight the disparity of experiences within communities and the need for kindness and understanding during what has been an unprecedented time. It seems to also capture and reflect our journey as an arts therapy team. Extracts from the poem will be quoted throughout this chapter, framing our experience during the UK national lockdown.

Our Context

The work detailed in this chapter comes from the viewpoint of an arts therapy team working in a special educational needs and disabilities (SEND) school. The school is part of a multi-academy trust, consisting of five schools with a central academy

DOI: 10.4324/9781003091783-20

therapy team. The school we focus on in this chapter educates pupils with severe to moderate learning difficulties between the ages 4 and 19 years. The arts therapy team across the academy consists of around 11 drama and music therapists, working in both individual and group contexts. The therapy team in each school aims to embed the child's therapy within their education and work with class teams to provide the appropriate support for each child referred to the therapy service.

The arts therapy team is also part of the central academy therapy team, which consists of all the therapies provided in our schools: Speech and Language Therapy (SaLT), Occupational Therapy (OT), Physiotherapy and Arts Therapy. The central team operates within a clear framework, allowing academy decisions and protocols to emerge and filter through a carefully designed model. We aim to put the children at the heart of everything we do and work together to provide the best opportunities for each pupil.

This chapter offers a reflection on our resilience as a team of therapists to work flexibly, while maintaining the boundaries we hold at the core of our practice, and to think creatively around therapy input during the first Covid-19 UK national lockdown. Included in this chapter are four specific case examples, two dramatherapy and two music therapy. These vignettes are examples of both the authors' clinical practice and highlight how arts therapy was made possible by the use of an online platform, enabling continued connection with clients and wider understanding of their world and relation to others.

Feeling the Turbulence

We are on different ships looking to survive.

The week of the 16 March 2020 is one etched in the minds of so many. It was the week before the UK went into strict lockdown due to the Covid-19 pandemic and the threat of the virus was completely uncertain; none of us knew the impact it would have on the entire world. SEND schools were presented with particular challenges, and it was an anxiety-provoking environment to be in for staff and students alike.

For many, it felt like systems were collapsing around us – concerned for jobs, loved ones and the potential threat of isolation and illness. Fear was 'loud' and all communication uncertain; we were told school could close for up to 12 weeks, and at the time, this felt incomprehensible. As an arts therapy team, we grappled with the inability to say goodbye to some clients and end sessions as we normally would; no countdown charts, no processing endings, all usual therapeutic rhythms rudely interrupted by the threat of a global pandemic.

As school-based arts therapists, we were aware of holding others' emotions; the weight of fear and panic felt heavy both individually and collectively. We wanted to support other staff members and protect the students but struggled when the daily reality meant hand sanitiser had run out and we had limited access to soap, unsettling when the clearest instruction was to keep washing your hands.

On Friday 20th March, school shut its doors and the arts therapy team were scattered, isolated in our homes and unsure of how we would continue working with clients. In those first few weeks of lockdown, many of us were sitting with the shock of what had happened. We had walked the uncertainty together at school and then suddenly found ourselves alone with our computers, feeling a sense of helplessness, yet determined to find a way to stay alongside the children, recreating a heavily relational job online.

Responding to the Surge

Some were in their 'home office'. Others looking through trash to survive.

When initially thinking about ways in which we could continue working, there seemed to be a wall of impossibility ahead of us. How could we communicate with children with a variety of communication difficulties, via the internet? How could we engage without intruding or overwhelming? Would families be able to access the internet and online platforms? The questions and dilemmas continued and answers were scarce. How could we navigate these turbulent waters? We realised we needed time to breathe and take in the scale of the situation and then, hopefully, solutions and ideas would begin to emerge.

From the outset, we were clear that our intervention should cause minimal disruption to the families. Therefore, it was initially established that the class teacher would be the only point of contact for each child. This meant we needed clear strategies and ideas before we approached staff. The central academy therapy team proved to be a crucial factor in this transition, as it became a clear channel of communication back to class teams. Prior to lockdown, we had met once a month at school with other therapists to discuss with children who were in need of extra support. However, once in lockdown, it was clear that weekly, more focused meetings were needed to join up the support offered to families.

Our weekly meetings consisted of:

- Therapy Link: A multidisciplinary meeting with SaLT/OT/Senior management/ family services/arts therapy
- Arts therapy team meeting: all arts therapists within the academy from across different schools
- School-specific meetings for the arts therapy teams: check-in around our wellbeing and progress

The weekly 'Therapy link' meetings provided us with an invaluable place to discuss children of immediate concern, ensuring the 'creative interchange in the service of the wellbeing of the patients', that Alison Davies (2015, 146) highlights. All therapy disciplines now had a shared focus, which was simply the well-being of each child, rather than goal-based targets. This meant that action plans could be created with confidence, knowing that individual knowledge and skills had been combined to give a holistic view of the child and their needs. From here, we were able to think about how the arts therapy team could offer support.

The weekly arts therapy team meetings became a space to devise new therapeutic resources and support for the children and families in our schools, examples of which will be shown in the vignettes further on in this chapter. The academy initiative was to spearhead a Parents Forum for which short, helpful, inventive and supportive videos were made across the whole therapy service (Eden 2020). These collaborative videos were an inspiration to us all, in which we modelled interaction and play through our different arts therapy modalities. From there, we were able to think about what could be possible, in terms of live online sessions with the children and families.

By week 3, we were starting to establish contact with many children and families from our individual caseloads, with the knowledge that we had thought through all the implications of therapy in the children's home environment through our academy structure. Initially, contact was made through phone calls, in which we began to absorb the dynamics in the home and connect with families in new ways. We held in mind the fact that many of the families we work with are especially vulnerable to social isolation (Barton 2007), potentially confined to small spaces and often supporting multiple children with varying additional needs and challenging behaviours.

During this brief period, we were able to offer families various suggestions and creative interventions, which were gratefully received. It seemed that simply knowing someone cared about their well-being and mental health, created a much-needed sense of connection, reducing isolation and anxiety.

Weathering the Storm

Let everyone navigate their route with respect, empathy and responsibility

It did not take long before children were requesting, or taking up our offers, of weekly Zoom (2021) sessions. Initially, our expectations of what would be possible for arts therapy online were limited. We struggled to imagine how an embodied creative session could unfold, given that so many of the children have moderate to severe communication difficulties. After gaining consent from parents/caregivers and agreeing that they would be present for sessions due to safeguarding protocols, work could begin. We invited the parents/caregivers to be alongside the child in their process in a way that felt comfortable for them. We also encouraged parents to be aware of their own reactions and notice when they felt the urge to control, suppress or divert the child's behaviour. We were delighted that so many families welcomed us into their home via Zoom and soon became fascinated by what started to emerge.

Once the children could physically see us, albeit via a camera lens, they spontaneously leapt into interaction and play. It felt as if the child took our hands and said, 'Of course I can do this, I remember what we did and what we can do together'. Separate to other online lessons the child may be receiving in the week, the therapy sessions became a 'permission giving' space for self-expression, with no goals or targets. The children found ways to explore their internal world, inside their own homes, with their parents/caregivers alongside them. The willing and playful response to this new set up, often, took us by surprise and allowed everyone involved to see things in a new and different light.

As the online therapy sessions gathered pace, it became apparent that bringing in this new dynamic did not fundamentally change the shape of the sessions. In fact, they were remarkably similar to those held in school. The aims and ways of working remained the same; the difference being that parents/caregivers not only witnessed our interaction but on occasion, became part of the creative play itself. To enable this play, both therapist and child made use of creative resources found at home such as playdough, art materials, Lego, instruments, figurines and books.

With familiar structures and boundaries in place, the therapeutic relationship continued to evolve online as it would in the therapy room. Organic improvisation, play, art, music, dance and dialogue emerged through affect attunement (Stern 1985) and our embodied responses (Bloom 2006) to the children. Active listening, matching, reflecting and responding to the children's cues were integral to this process. Therefore, the lack of physical proximity in the therapy room did not dissolve the sense of intimacy we could create. As worlds were closing in and everyday life became increasingly restricted, we were able to open up a potential space (Winnicott 1971) for the children to access their internal world and process their emotional responses to the pandemic.

Despite our own initial questioning and doubt that online sessions could be a progressive part of our clients' therapy, we were reminded to 'trust the process'. We were not just 'holding' (Winnicott 1990) the space in order to maintain a relationship but also offering a contained (Bion 1962) and safe environment in which existing relationships could develop and new connections could be established.

It is important to note that not all children found it easy to engage; some with high sensory needs became overstimulated, and others found it challenging to maintain focus. In these instances, we still offered tailored support and tried to ensure that we did not create further disruption to the family, in an already trying time.

In the following section, we provide case examples through four clinical vignettes reflecting the reality of sessions in lockdown, spotlighting moments of challenge and progress. We include considerations on how these sessions enhanced our understanding of each child and shaped our therapeutic relationship. Pseudonyms have been used to protect the client's identity.

How Online Dramatherapy Sessions Strengthened Relationships and Modelled Ways of Creative Play within the Home

David

David has a diagnosis of autism. He has received arts therapy intervention since joining the school as a young infant. For safety, his initial arts therapy sessions were held by two therapists (music and drama), due to unpredictable, chaotic and often very violent outbursts both in school and at home. David continually struggles with self-esteem and will often refer to himself as a failure. In his initial creative therapy sessions, David would give continuous directions and could easily erupt into rage and violence if he felt misunderstood in any way. He struggled with any form of transition and repeated rituals numerous times before he could move from one activity to the next. I worked 1:1 with David for over two years before lockdown, and we had gradually formed a trusting relationship in which he had begun to develop shared play skills and find ways to manage transitions with greater ease.

In the first two weeks of lockdown, his Mum reported that her family were struggling and she desperately needed support. David did not want to leave the house. He would regularly implode with rage, and often, the only way to calm him would be to give him his iPad. Relationships had broken down and the situation felt helpless. Before my first online session with David, I remembered his love of playdough and gave an easy homemade recipe (via the class teacher) to Mum. As soon as the session started, David immediately engaged and wanted to use this homemade playdough. He remembered the 'McDonalds Drive-through' improvisation we had created in our previous sessions in school and soon set about shaping and creating Burgers, Fries and Shakes: all made from colourful dough. We then re-enacted driving through, to place our order. His hands would reach to the screen to offer the food he had made. David squealed with delight, laughing in many moments as I pretended to scoff the food and comment on how yummy it was. His mother became very engaged with the play and often shared words of encouragement and praise to her son as the role play unfolded. At another point in the session, David spontaneously asked for a 'dance off'; I followed his lead, his mother quickly rearranged the living room furniture and the dance off commenced. David requested I 'beat box', so he could show me his moves first. His moves were so expressive and energised. We then swapped the activity around and I jumped into action, David was full of praise for my dancing, and Mum was clearly very amused at my silly display. At the end of the session, David reminded me that we would be meeting at the same time next week and shared lots of ideas about what we could do together. He commented that the time together had helped him to feel calm and feel much better about himself.

After this session, David had a renewed sense of vitality; permission had been given for us all to play together and magical moments of shared creative expression, laughter and joy appeared. He felt valued and his ideas had been met with eagerness and enthusiasm. The iPad had been put down, dynamics had shifted and new ideas were emerging. Mum had a moment to breathe and see things through a different lens. Due to Mum witnessing and joining the play, a deeper level of trust had been established between us. As a result, I spoke with her every week, following David's return to school, providing a much-needed channel of communication and support through a very turbulent time.

How Online Music Therapy Sessions Provided Insight into Home Life and Contributed to Co-Working Strategies

Hiran

Prior to lockdown, Hiran and I had six sessions together at school, within which he explored the therapy space and used the instruments to express himself, often in very forceful ways. He would positively engage in the music and then suddenly switch to throwing instruments around, needing my support to regulate and continue the session safely.

When lockdown hit, I found myself often wondering how his family was coping. He lives with his parents and four older siblings (one of whom also has SEND) in a small flat with no garden. Confined conditions for anyone, let alone a child with autism and communication difficulties.

After a month of lockdown, I began to try contacting Hiran's parents. This proved harder than anticipated, and it took quite a few attempts before I got through to them. I set up a Zoom session with Mum and logged into our first call, unsure of what I might be met with.

For the first two Zoom appointments, Hiran did not appear. I called Mum and no one answered. On the third week of trying, they logged on; there he was, staring at me on the screen. I sang our 'hello' song and Mum waved at me, trying to encourage Hiran to do so too, but he was already up and running around the room. He pushed the device over, shouting and pulling at his Mum and his siblings, some of whom were also in the room. It was hard to witness this level of distress, and I suggested that we end the call. Hiran's Mum managed to calm him down by singing 'The Wheels on the Bus'. We sang this together, and Hiran even did some of the actions. A glimpse of connection and then he was up and off round the room again. Mum said to him: 'If you sit down and do music therapy, I'll give you a chocolate bar'. He sat down in response to this and listened to another song before getting up again. Mum tried to bribe him once more and then gave up, apologised to me and ended the call.

I sat in silence, stunned by how chaotic our first session had been. The bribes from Mum happened throughout the rest of our sessions together and seeing her try and contain Hiran was hard.

Hiran's transition back to school post-lockdown was difficult. For the first few weeks, he ran around the school and playground, unable to be in the classroom without disturbing other children or injuring members of staff. Our sessions on Zoom had given me a glimpse into his chaotic world, and as a result, I was able to give feedback to colleagues on Hiran's home life and family situation.

Through conversation with his class team, OT and SaLT, strategies were devised to help support Hiran access school; this has included always having an adult hold his hand and reassure him as he makes transitions, consistent approaches to ending activities with preparation for what follows and a balance of time in and out of class.

I have continued these strategies in music therapy and now always have a member of class walk with him to and from sessions and use a countdown approach that is being consistently used elsewhere. It has by no means been a quick fix: there are still days when he struggles to access the classroom and therapy sessions, but by using the knowledge gained through Zoom of his home life, we have been able to put boundaries in place which will hopefully continue to support his development and growth.

How Online Dramatherapy Sessions Provided Greater Context around a Child's Communication Patterns

Varsha

Varsha has received arts therapy since arriving at the school aged seven years old. She had been referred due to poor communication skills, which had often resulted in extreme behaviour in the classroom. After a short period of time in a small group, it was decided she would benefit from 1:1 dramatherapy. Before the national lockdown, our sessions had been running for over two years; during this time, an established, trusting bond had been built between us. The family has English as their second language, and I relied upon an interpreter when communicating with them.

When starting my sessions with Varsha, it became clear that she suffered from profound hearing loss, and that somehow the severity of her impairment had not been identified as a possible reason for her extreme behaviours. Because she had been so hard to engage, much time and focus had been spent calming her and working through explosive outbursts. As a result, she had not developed any consistent means of communication and had become very reliant on making exaggerated facial expressions and loud vocal sounds as a way of gaining attention. When conveying this back to the central therapy team, provisions were immediately put in place for Varsha to build her communication vocabulary at school.

As we built our therapeutic relationship, through embodied communication, I noticed she had a great sense of humour and a well-developed sense of empathy. This allowed for a variety of relational role-plays to emerge in the therapy space. Many imagined scenarios were set up in our sessions; we would create school classrooms in which she delighted in playing the 'Teacher', 'Hairdressing Salons' in which she took the part of 'Senior Stylist', musical shows in which we were both the stars and 'Shopping Centres' in which she would be the very chatty till lady or customer. The words she used were occasionally intelligible, but usually, it was just an array of appropriate expressive sounds and gestures.

When thinking about Zoom as a replacement for these sessions, my heart skipped a beat. How could I work with a nine-year-old girl with profound hearing loss via Zoom? However, as soon as our faces appeared on the screens, the desire to create and play leapt into the online space between us. A member of her family stood patiently by her side (off screen) and the play commenced. She was initially exceptionally keen to show me her toys and create her imaginary 'Toy Shop'. I had been given the role of customer and my responses to the objects for sale were gratefully received. She then communicated to her family member that she wanted her dance game to be put on the TV and showed me how she could follow the routines, delighting in each sequence of Bhangra dances, eagerly awaiting her applause. Her family members also showed appreciation through their reactions, and I could feel the warmth and joy in the room as she took her bow. In this moment, I captured a unique glimpse into family culture as well as aspects of the dynamics in the house. Many spontaneous moments like this arose in our sessions.

In other moments, I observed her difficulty when other family members were busily chatting on their phones, I felt her confusion and desire to try and understand what was happening around her. I noticed ways in which she made loud vocal and bodily gestures in order to feel seen and heard. The extreme behaviours we had initially witnessed when she joined the school had renewed context and week by week a picture emerged.

Before these Zoom sessions, Varsha's means of communication at home had been unclear. It had largely been a guessing game, contact with the family being minimal and they were hard to engage. Now I had been able to observe that the language spoken at home was not a mode of communication for her, and she relied entirely on bodily gestures and sounds to communicate. These sessions became a unique gift that provided much-needed insight to Varsha's family environment. Now pieces of the puzzle had slotted into place, and Varsha knew that some of her frustrations had been witnessed and understood. Important information had been gathered and translated back to the staff team. On her return to school, with new approaches to her educational environment embedded, we witnessed a significant decrease in her levels of frustration. She has engaged with enthusiasm in nearly all aspects of her school life this year.

How Online Music Therapy Sessions Demonstrated a Child's Potential to Play and Interact

Jess

I had worked with Jess for five weeks before lockdown in early 2020, and these sessions were each a whirlwind. It had taken her two weeks to actually make it into the therapy room; once she was there, she used the space in a very expressive and unpredictable way, often banging drums with much force and then throwing down the drumsticks, running round the room and then posting instruments out of the window. I worked in the room with Jess and one of the teaching assistants from her class, with whom she already had a strong relationship.

Jess is verbal but uses few words and often shouts her own name. In sessions at school, she seemed unable to play with us and was very much following her own agenda.

Once in lockdown, I wondered how Jess' family would be coping at home in a small space with her unpredictable behaviour. I waited a few weeks before reaching out to Jess' mother via her class teacher, and both were keen to try and make music therapy work online. I asked the teaching assistant I had worked with at school if she would be available to join our Zoom sessions, and she was willing to be involved.

Each session was different depending on Jess' emotional state that day, but one of our online sessions remains memorable. Jess was very focused and calm and vocalised all our names in the 'hello' song, which had never happened in our sessions at school. There was then spontaneous musical turn-taking between the class assistant and Jess, as they both played their own recorders and stared at the screen. It happened completely unprompted, and Mum, teaching assistant and I were surprised and delighted with how Jess had picked up on the turn-taking and continued the play.

Reflecting each week with the teaching assistant provided an opportunity to debrief and share our thoughts on how the session had gone. After this particular session, both of us were very moved by how Jess had engaged and could not believe how focused and calm she had been, a complete contrast to how she normally presents at school. The Zoom sessions continued to feel positive and provided Jess a space to engage with us musically and also for Mum to witness her development and what could be possible for Jess with support and further therapy provision.

Acclimatising to the New Landscape

It is very important to see beyond what is seen at first glance.
Not just looking, more than looking...

Aspects from this time of working on Zoom have already started to shape us as practitioners, and moving forward, we want to capture and mark these as a team. The use of Zoom has given us a window into the child's world, and thinking has begun around how to hold onto the benefits of working in this way.

Attachment (Bowlby 2005) between child and caregivers had been observed in a very real way, which would not necessarily have happened without this sudden need to use online platforms for our therapeutic intervention. Levels of understanding have been fast-tracked through observing the child's interactions and levels of play. Many facets of the child's social and emotional world had been revealed, which previously took considerable time to uncover. Parents/siblings/ caregivers often became an extension of the therapist's hands, eyes and ears, being alongside the child physically: holding or containing where necessary. As a result, we are considering the use of online assessments in their homes before arts therapy input commences: a potential way to gain insight into the child's attachment as well as collaborating effectively with families.

Flexibility has been integral in enabling therapeutic input to take place. Being able to bend the ways we frame sessions and work creatively online has led to a broader view of how we approach therapy, and this has continued on return to school. The work that emerged as a result of all of us being forced into our homes has highlighted the essentials of what we need to work effectively as therapists: a safe therapeutic space, a client, a way of connecting with them and a creative way of expressing ourselves together to enrich the therapeutic relationship.

Working remotely has also highlighted the benefit and importance of belonging to a team of therapists. Meeting together as a whole team prior to lockdown happened once a term, as we all work different days across different schools. This changed in lockdown, and more frequently, set Zoom team meetings have continued, providing a time to check-in and share any important information; something which perhaps sounds obvious, but for a large team working across multiple schools, it has become a lifeline.

Rainbow after the Storm

We are going through a time when our perceptions and needs are completely different. And each one will emerge, in his own way, from that storm.

When reflecting, in various teams, across the academy, it has been clear to us that despite the difficulties and challenges that resulted from the Covid-19 pandemic, we emerge 'in our own way', as transformed and different clinicians.

Just as we were finishing writing this chapter, we had to return to working online during the third lockdown in England. The transition back to online working felt surprisingly smooth, and we were able to reach out to most children quickly and effectively. We recognise the challenges online platforms present to the therapeutic relationship: questions around safeguarding, privacy and confidentiality – not forgetting the ever-present threat of the unreliability of online connection. We were working with limited resources, and we missed the physical, embodied, shared space, losing the literal boundaries of the therapy room. These are all issues regularly discussed and debated within both personal and team supervision. However, our practice and lives will be forever changed and shaped by this time, in both collectively positive and personally heavy ways. To make it through, we have needed to see beyond the initial chaos, to see beyond the boundaries we held so tightly to and to see beyond difference and challenge.

This storm will eventually end, and we will perhaps look back and see not only the challenges, loss, grief and separation that everyone has gone through in this time, but perhaps also see how we, as arts therapists, have been shaped by the need for flexibility, creativity and compassion like never before.

References

Barr, D. 2020. [Twitter] 6 December. Available at: https://twitter.com/damian_barr/status/1335638579263893505 (Accessed 6 January 2021).

Barton, P. 2007. *Letting go, understanding your young child with special needs.* London: Jessica Kingsley.

Bion, W. R. 1962. 'A theory of thinking.' In: *International Journal of Psychoanalysis.* Volume 43, 306–310. Taylor and Francis Online.

Bloom, K. 2006. *The embodied self,* London: Karnac Books.

Bowlby, J. 2005. *The making and breaking of affectional bonds* (1976–1977). London: Taylor and Francis (Books) Limited.

Davies, A. 2015. 'Co-therapy and working with others.' In: Richard, E., Davies, A. & Barwick, N. (Eds.) *Group music therapy – a group analytic approach.* 140–146. London and New York: Routledge.

Eden Academy Trust. 2020. *Emotional Wellbeing* https://theedenacademy.co.uk/parent-pages/ (Accessed 19 November 2021).

Stern, D. 1985. *The four senses of self, the interpersonal world of the infant: a view from psychoanalysis and developmental psychology.* London: Karnac Books.

Winnicott, D. W. 1971. *Playing and reality.* London: Tavistock Publications

Winnicott, D. W. 1990. 'The theory of parent-infant relationship'. In: Winnicott, D. W. (Ed.) *The maturational processes and the facilitating environment: studies in the theory of emotional development.* 49. London: Karnac.

Zoom Video Communications. 2021. *Video Conferencing, Cloud Phone, Webinars, Chat, Virtual Events | Zoom.* [online] Available at: https://zoom.us/ (Accessed 3 September 2021).

Conclusion

Helen Milward

I wish to start this conclusion, by thanking the contributing authors of this book. It has been an honour and a privilege to have been witness to the stories, experiences, journeys and explorations gifted to us by working with this client group. I hope the reader gains as much understanding, knowledge and enthusiasm as I have while compiling this book. It depicts a rich world of work within this field, and I am greatly encouraged by the passion demonstrated in wanting to give voice to this client group.

The many 'voices' represented in this book reflect epic journeys of self-discovery, development and identity, for both the client and the therapist. The compassion and care for the client group shines through as all the authors describe their work in creating these rewarding relationships.

This book has outlined the context and provisions for people with learning disabilities, educationally, developmentally and socially. It has explored the capacity for feeling and being with oneself and others, understanding and empathy with learning disabilities, emotional distress and difficulties with mental health and how we see those with learning disabilities. It has examined the continual need for therapists to be flexible in their approach to work, offering unconditional positive regard, and has explored how people with learning disabilities may access dramatherapy for 'treatment' for the mental health issues or distress they may experience, or as part of proactive life education, in which creativity enables a connection to the parts of the self that heal and create good health.

A variety of themes have been identified in different chapters but with many commonalities weaving through the encounters with this client group. There is an important recognition of this client group's struggle to find their place, to have a voice, to be seen and heard. The emphasis here is on their advocacy aided by multidisciplinary professionals working collaboratively together. Through providing bespoke interventions, in which systems and institutions offer connections based on individual needs, people with learning disabilities can find validation and work towards acceptance, both internally and externally.

The unique relationships and environments created through dramatherapy allow for the time and patience needed to attune to and encourage clients, in order to build confidence, self-esteem and freedom to explore choice and life experiences.

DOI: 10.4324/9781003091783-21

Dramatherapists' flexibility and ability to adapt, while offering consistency, familiarity and rituals, creates an environment of respect and curiosity. This enables the safe exploration of feelings of shame, judgement and disconnectedness, while promoting a sense of appreciation and celebration of the individual.

All of these themes weave themselves through this book, as the authors reflect on their experiences within the field. These themes, it could be argued, are common to all human beings, but for those with learning disabilities, I come back to the Mencap definition that, 'People with a learning disability tend to take longer to learn and may need support to develop new skills, understand complicated information and interact with other people' (Mencap, 2020). It is not surprising that a common thread throughout all the chapters centres on relationships, systemic interventions and multi-professional cooperation to contribute to development and transformation.

The progression of people with learning disabilities towards finding a place in society has been gradual, but the chapters of this book highlight that society-wide understanding and acceptance still has a long way to go. There is still much need for further research and exploration into the social, emotional and mental health development of those with learning disabilities; to increase awareness of mental health-related issues for those with learning disabilities; for advocacy to give people with learning disabilities a 'voice' – be this a verbal or non-verbal expression – and a wider communication of what those with learning disabilities can accomplish, so that they can have a greater quality of life and make a contribution within society. This book has explored what the role of the dramatherapist is within this process, and how therapy can take a proactive part in a person's life and extend the capacity to be with oneself and others with dignity and a sense of equality.

Reference

Mencap (2020). *What is a Learning Disability? https://www.mencap.org.uk/learning-disability-explained/what-learning-disability* Accessed 14 June 2023

Index

Note: *Italic* page numbers refer to figures.

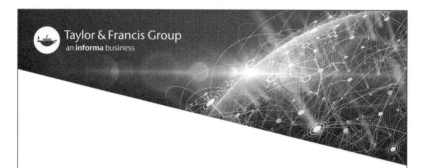